DINO-MUSCLES ®

& CITY KIDZ STEP ™

A Comprehensive Fitness, Wellness & Edu-tainment Program For Today's Youth

City KidZStep™ by
Debbie Ban-Pillarella, M.Ed.

Dino-Muscles® by
Andrew Paul Bonsall

Published by Know Books
in cooperation with Danella Soeka, Visual Difference

Animal Illustrations by Sue Montalbano
Dino-Muscles Illustrations by Courtney Hay
Edited by Richard Ban & Laura Ingratta

City KidZStep

Copyright © 1993 BodyWorks, Inc.

The name City KidZStep may not be used in the titles, descriptions, or advertising of your youth fitness program.

FOR INFORMATION CONTACT:

BodyWorks
12916 Commercial
Chicago, Illinois 60633
312-646-5954

A special thanks to my husband, Jim, and my parents, Richard and Josephine Ban for believing in me and supporting all my endeavors. For without you, this manual would not be possible.

WHAT THE KIDS ARE SAYING . . .

"I thought this was going to be real boring; I hate to exercise. But it wasn't. It's the best! It's fun. I love it"

Mark Olguin, 5 year old

"I never knew exercising could be so much fun. KidZ Step is AWESOME!

Julio Tenorio, 9 years old

"KidZ Step gives me muscles and makes my heart strong. Plus, it's a BLAST!

Eva Tello, 11 years old

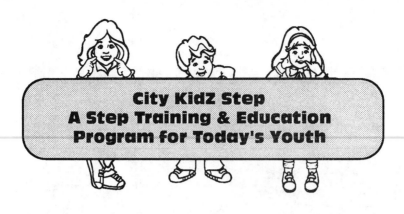

City KidZ Step
A Step Training & Education
Program for Today's Youth

TABLE OF CONTENTS

Mission Statement

City KidZ Step

A fun-filled fitness and health program for today's youth . . . tomorrow's future!!!

Education for a healthy mind and body empowers today's youth with the knowledge and attitudes necessary to lead a positive lifestyle into adulthood. Education can only be of value to the youth of today if it is MEANINGFUL and FUN. It is the goal of this program to provide a fun-filled physical learning environment that will promote positive health habits and attitudes throughout life.

OVERALL OBJECTIVES

The youth participants will be able to do the following upon completion of this program:

- Demonstrate at least five fun movements that are non-stop and heart healthy.

- Demonstrate at least five safe and effective stepping techniques.

- Successfully complete an exercise workout appropriate for each level.

- Work cooperatively with other children.

- Successfully complete the muscle strengthening component with proper form and execution.

- Correctly execute muscle strengthening exercises using the SPRI QuikFit.

- Correctly identify at least five muscles of the body that are used in this program.

- Correctly name at least five benefits of this program in regard to overall health and well being.

- Correctly identify at least three muscles and their functions from the Dino-Muscles™ Lessons.

- Participate in daily Kid Rap sessions.

- Record his/her own progress daily.

PROGRAM OVERVIEW

*T*he Program is divided into separate grade driven curricula. Acknowledging the research on the attention span of children, each program is planned for 15-20 minutes for Early Childhood, 20-30 minutes for ages 6-9, and 40-45 minutes for ages 10-12. Activities alternate between aerobic "playful" moves and strength/endurance moves every few minutes.

*T*he Early Childhood Level is for ages 3-5. At this level, the children are engaged in both group and circuit-style classes. Young children are natural "interval" movers; therefore, it is imperative that the activity be continuously changing. Early Childhood KidZ Step uses the 26 letters of the alphabet, represented by animals to teach step and non-step activities to be used in a group format. Letter Sounds, rhyming, singing, and movement are taught at this level. Each animal corresponds to a letter of the alphabet (i.e. A=Alligator, D=Dog). The animal is stepping to his favorite rhyme, which is set to the melody of famous children's songs. The children enjoy singing along as they move to the "Animal Beat". Coordination, balance, kinesthetic awareness and motor skill development are all addressed.

*L*evel 1, ages 6-10, are engaged in fun-filled movements and exercises using the Dino-Muscles™ characters. Each dinosaur is featured as the children learn about their bodies and move to the "Dino-beat".

*L*evel 2, ages 10-12, uses "child-selected" music coordinated with step moves and strength/endurance exercises in a group format alternated with circuit activities. The step moves selected represent familiar moves the children use in sports, like the Football V, Batter Up, Karate Kick, and Basketball Shoot, as well as dance, like the MC Hammer Hop, and Cowboy Straddle.

*K*id Rap, concludes each daily session. Children rap about topics relevant to their life, as well as concepts that teach them about health and fitness. The Dino-Muscles™ health curriculum teaches the children anatomical and kinesiological concepts through the fun use of dinosaurs. The vibrant color-filled dinosaur characters bring theory to life and provide the excitement children need to understand these concepts.

A note about Heart Rates . . .
Children are naturally spontaneous and sporadic movers. Therefore, they rarely engage in any activity for a long period of time without stopping. It seems needless to have children monitor their pulses. Additionally, how could we ever begin to think that they could monitor it accurately if and when they did find it? For this reason, it is recommended that children perceive how they feel and make sure they can "talk" to each other throughout any playful activities or exercises. It is also important to allow for sufficient rehydration as children easily overheat due to the continual development of their thermoregulatory systems.

What It's All About

The entire City KidZ Step Program is based on the current philosophies and theories in education that focus on meaningful, active, and full-filled activities connected to the children's home environment.

THIS PROGRAM IS:

*A*CTIVE
   All children are involved simultaneously in activity.

*M*OTIVATING
   All children receive motivational rewards and incentives for participating.

*I*NTERDISCIPLINARY
   The children engage in reading, mathematics, music, dance, art, science, and social studies while enjoying KidZ Step.

*M*ULTIDIMENSIONAL
   The children learn through a variety of dimensions: Auditory, Visual, and Kinesthetic.

*P*OSITIVE MODELING
   Through the physical educator's participation and coaching, KidZ Step provides for positive modeling of successful behaviors, a must for transfer of learning to occur.

*E*MPOWERING
   The children gain power by becoming responsible for their own physical, psychological, and emotional growth and development.

*C*OOPERATIVE
   KidZ Step participants work non-competitively with partners or in small group environments.

*C*ONNECTED
   KidZ Step moves, music, and themes have been developed <u>by children, for children,</u> which ensures that it is FUN!!!!!

Early Childhood Step - Preschoolers
Lesson Plan Overview

	KidZ Step	Circuit	Kid Rap
Week 1	Songs 1 & 2		1
Week 2		X	2
Week 3	Songs 3 & 4		3
Week 4		X	4
Week 5	Songs 5 & 6		5
Week 6		X	6
Week 7	Songs 7 & 8		9
Week 8		X	11
Week 9	Songs 9 & 10		1
Week 10		X	2
Week 11	Songs 11 & 12		3
Week 12		X	4
Week 13	Songs 13 & 14		5
Week 14		X	6
Week 15	Songs 15 & 16		9
Week 16		X	11
Week 17	Songs 17 & 18		Your Choice
Week 18		X	↓
Week 19	Songs 19/20/21		
Week 20		X	↓

KIDZ Step - Level 1 and Level 2
Lesson Plan Overview

LEVEL 1 (ages 6-9)

	KidZ Step	Circuit	Kid Rap
Week 1	X		1,2
Week 2		X	3,4
Week 3	X		5,6
Week 4		X	7
Week 5	X		8
Week 6		X	9 & 10
Week 7	X		10
Week 8		X	10

LEVEL 2 (ages 10-12)

	Testing	KidZ Step	Circuit	Kid Rap
Pre Program	*X			
Week 1		X		1,2
Week 2			X	3,4
Week 3		X		5,6
Week 4			X	7,8
Week 5		X		9
Week 6			X	10
Week 7		X		10 & 11
Week 8			X	10 & 12
Post Program	*X			

* Use AAPHERD'S Physical Best of YMCA'S Youth Fitness Testing Program
 (see Section 10)

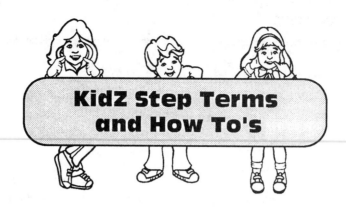

KidZ Step Terms and How To's

* All step movements are executed in sets. Each set consists of 8 counts of music. For example, 1 set of Basic Steps would be 8 counts or Up Up Down Down, Up Up Down Down.

* All KidZ Step exercises are executed in sets as well. Each set consists of 8 repetitions. For example: 1 set of Bicep BeBop would be equivalent to 8 bicep curls (one bicep curl = the curl up and the return to starting position)

All KidZ Step choreography has been Kid Tested and originates from the following basic moves.

LEAD FOOT
The foot that is responsible for beginning the movement/step. It is the first foot to start a movement or pattern.

BASIC STEP
Up, Up, Down, Down (either right or left lead).
     Ex. Right Leg Lead

JUMP STEP
Jump up and Hold for 1 count atop the step, step Down, Down.

DOUBLE STEP
Up, Up, March atop step (count 3,4,5,6,7,8).
Down, Down, March of the floor (count 3,4,5,6,7,8).

VICTORY STEP
Forming the letter V atop the step with your feet placement.
Up, Up, Down, Down
Ex. Right Leg Lead

"A" STEP
Begin standing on the floor near the left end of the step. Step up with the right foot (to the middle of the step). Step up with the left foot (to the middle of the step). Step down with the right foot (now on the floor near the right end of the step). Step down and tap left foot next to right foot. Repeat beginning with left foot.

NEUTRAL
A transition position which allows you to call a new move, i.e. change feet. Neutral position requires both feet to be doing the same thing simultaneously (tap toes, squats, hop in place, etc.)

ALTERNATING UP N KARATE KICK
With a right leg lead, step up with right foot, left foot kick, left foot steps down, right foot steps down (ready to step up with opposite foot). Step up with left foot, right foot kicks, right foot steps down, left foot steps down.

COWBOY STRADDLE
Begin standing atop the step facing the short end of the step. Straddle down. Right foot down on the right side of the step. Then place the left foot down on the left side of the step. Return the right foot up on top of the step. Then return the left foot to the top of the step.

STRADDLE KNEE

Begin standing atop the step, facing the short end of the step. Straddle down beginning with the right foot stepping down on the right side of the step. Then place the left foot down on the left side of the step. Return the right foot to the top of the step and lift the left knee. Return the left foot to the floor then the right foot steps down on the right side of the step. The left foot steps atop the step. Then lift the right knee. Repeat.

FOOTBALL V

This move is a variation of the Victory Step., Begin with both feet on the floor.
Right foot up, left foot up (to form a V atop the step)
Football jog atop the step (count 5,6,7,8)
Right foot steps down, left foot steps down
Football job on the floor (count 5,6,7,8)

BATTER UP

The feet begin next to the step facing the short side. Move across the top of the step in three counts and tap down the foot closest to the step on the 4th count and repeat.
Right foot up, left foot up (you are now atop the step), right foot steps down (on right side of step), left foot taps down next to step (on right side of step).
Moving back across the top to your starting position.
Left foot up, right foot up (you are now atop the step). Left foot steps down (on left side of step), right foot taps down next to the step (on left side of step).

*Arms hold an imaginary baseball bat on the first three counts. Arms swing the imaginary bat on the fourth count.

ALTERNATING VOLLEYBALL SET

Begin facing the step.
Right foot steps up, left foot steps up. (count 1,2,)
Squat atop step, come up on toes and simulate a volleyball set up with arms (count 3,4,)
Right foot steps down, Left foot steps down.
Squat (on floor), come up on toes and simulate a volleyball set up with arms.
    *Repeat with left foot leading

LUNGE AWAY

Begin atop the step.
Lunge down (foot comes in contact with the floor) with right foot, return.
Right foot atop the step.
Lunge down with left foot, return left foot atop the step.

BASKETBALL SHOOT

This is a variation of the Karate Kick.
Begin facing the step.
Step up with the right foot.
Lift the left knee and shoot arms as if shooting a basketball.
Step down with left foot.
Tap right foot down on the floor.

**ALTERNATING
BASKETBALL SHOOT**

This is a variation of the Alternating Karate Kick.
Begin facing the step.
Step up with the right foot.
Lift the left knee and shoot arms as if shooting a basketball.
Step down with left foot.
Step down with right foot (to change lead legs).

Step up with the left foot.
Lift the right knee and shoot arms as if shooting a basketball.
Step down with right foot.
Step down with left foot (to repeat from beginning).

**ALTERNATING
BOOGIE HEEL**

This is a variation of the Karate Kick.
Begin facing the step.
Right foot steps up.
Tap left heel atop the step.
Step down with left foot.
Bring right foot down to hop in place twice (this switches you to other lead leg).

Left foot steps up.
Tap right heel atop the step.
Step down with right foot.
Bring right foot down to hop in place twice.

LOOK OUT

A neutral position atop the step or on the floor.
Execute small squats looking right and left with
hand above eyes (as if looking away in the distance).

Exercise
How To's

NOTE: Some of the following exercises have two titles depending on their age appropriateness. All exercises should be executed in sets of 4 or 8 repetitions. Remember to balance the workout by completing the same number of repetitions on both sides of the body (i.e. right arm/left arm).

Bicep Beebop (Level 1) • Bicep Curls (Level 2)

(LEFT) Begin with one end of the QuikFit under the right foot. The other end is in the right hand. The elbow is resting comfortably on the hip.

(RIGHT) Exhale while contracting the bicep muscle. Pull the QuikFit toward the right shoulder, keeping the elbow comfortably on the hip.
Hold, return to starting position and repeat.
Complete equal sets with both arms.

Da Deltoids (Level 1) • Shoulder Raises (Level 2)

(LEFT) Begin with one end of the QuikFit securely under one foot. The other end is gently grasped by both hands.

(RIGHT) Keeping the wrists straight, exhale and contract the deltoids, causing the hands to come under the chin. The elbows pointing toward the ceiling and the shoulders are down and relaxed.
Hold, return to starting position, and repeat.

9

TraZapius (Level 1 • Trapezius Pull Backs (Level 2)

(LEFT) Begin with both arms outstretched in front of the body. The QuikFit is held comfortably in each hand, wrists straight.

(RIGHT) Exhale and contract the trapezius muscles as the right arm pulls the QuikFit toward the back of body. Keep torso steady, shoulders down and relaxed, and elbow pointing toward the back. Hold, return to starting position and repeat.

Tricep Truffle Punch (Level 1) • Tricep Extension (Level 2)

(LEFT) Begin holding the QuikFit in each hand. Each hand is placed on the front of the shoulders, elbows pointing downward.

(RIGHT) Exhale while contracting the triceps. Extend one arm to the side, wrist straight, and palm pointing downward. Hold, return to starting position and repeat. Complete equal sets with both arms.

10

Pec"Turtal" is (Level 1) • Pectoralis Press (Level 2)

(LEFT) Begin with one end of the QuikFit in one hand and behind the back. The other end of the QuikFit is held in the hand.

(RIGHT) Keeping wrist straight, exhale, and contract the pectoral muscles as one arm comes around in front of the chest.
Hold, return to starting position, and repeat, with the other arm. Complete equal sets with both arms.

Quad Ra Bunga (Level 1) • Quadriceps (Level 2)

(LEFT) Begin standing next to step.

(RIGHT) Exhale as squatting with one foot atop the step.
Hold, return to starting position and repeat.
Complete equal sets with both legs.

*Keep knee in line with heel.

Modified Push Up (Levels 1 and 2)

(LEFT Photo) Begin kneeling on a mat behind step. Fingers facing forward, palms shoulder width apart, resting on top of the step.

(RIGHT Photo) Inhale and lower the chest toward the top of the step. Exhale as returning body to starting position. Repeat

Kid Crunch (Level 1) • Curl Ups (Level 2)

(LEFT Photo) Lay supine atop a mat, knees bent, feet flat on the floor. The hands should cradle the head.

(RIGHT Photo) Exhale, contract abdominals and lift head and shoulders off floor. Avoid pulling on head/neck. Hold return to starting position and repeat.
*Note: If executing with a partner, slap hands (i.e. high-five) as curling up as demonstrated in the photo.

Twist N Shake (Level 1) • Obliques (Level 2)

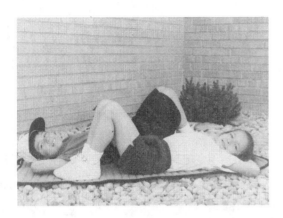

(LEFT Photo) Begin supine on mat, knees bent, feet flat on floor, hands comfortably cradle head.

(RIGHT Photo) Exhale, contract obliques and twist as flexing the trunk. Be careful not to rotate the hips. Complete sets for both sides of the body.
NOTE: If working with a partner, twist toward the partner and shake hands.

Whoa Horsey (Level 1) • Seated Shoulder Raises (Level 2)

(LEFT) Begin sitting on the step, feet flat on the floor, knees bent, abdominals held in, body upright. One end of the QuikFit is under one foot, as the foot is in full contact with the floor. The other end is held, with the sponge handle in both hands, resting on the lap.

(RIGHT) Exhale as the QuikFit is pulled upright, hands coming toward the chin. Elbows are pointing toward the ceiling, shoulders are kept down, deltoids are contracting. Hold and return to starting position. Repeat.

Double Row Boat (Level 1 & 2)

(LEFT Photo) Begin in a seated position with a partner. Working with a partner and two QuikFits; give one end of each QuikFit to your partner. The hands are resting on the lap.

(RIGHT Photo) Exhale and contract the upper back muscles as pulling the QuikFits up and back, adducting the shoulder blades. Both children must pull simultaneously. Hold and return to starting position. Repeat.

BiCep BeeBop (without the thumb gesture) • Hitch Hike (Level 1 & 2)

(LEFT) Begin sitting on the step, feet flat on the floor, abdominals held in, body upright. One end of the QuikFit is under the right foot, while foot maintains full contact with the floor. The other end of the QuikFit is in the right hand, hand resting on the lap, palm facing upward.

(RIGHT) Exhale and contract the biceps as moving the palm toward the shoulder. During the movement, turn the thumb outward, as simulating a "hitch hiker". Hold and return to starting position.
Repeat.
Complete equal sets with both arms.

14

Monster Scare (Level 1) • Chest Press (Level 2)

(LEFT Photo) Children are seated on steps with their backs to each other. One end of the QuikFit is in the right hand of one child and the left hand of the other child. The other QuikFit is in the left hand of the first child, and the right hand of the second. The QuikFits parallel each other.

(RIGHT Photo) Exhale and contract the pectoral and deltoid muscles as one child reaches the arms forward. The children can count 1-2-3-GO to help them with a smooth execution.
Take turns.

*For Monster Scare children make a yelling monster sound when reaching forward.

Kidz Step

EARLY CHILDHOOD AND LEVEL 1

The Early Childhood Level and Level 1 KidZ Step alternates between Group KidZ Step and CirKid KidZ Step (Section 5). The Group KidZ Step uses the following Kid Songs and accompanying choreography. The Group work occurs on alternate weeks (see Lesson Plan Overview Section 2). The Early Childhood program should be done for approximately 15-20 minutes per class. The Level 1 program should be done for 20-30 minutes per class.

The following items and Talk and Tell should be done with all lesson plans:

- Pass out handout
- Discuss letter identification
- Read the caption
- Color the picture

Talk and Tell

At the end of each session, let the children talk and tell their favorite "fact" about the animal and movement of the day. They can share this information to the entire class or to their friends.

* Note: By the time the entire program has been taught, the children will have learned all the letters of the alphabet, their phonetic sounds, animal facts and many reading and language arts skills.

LESSON PLAN
Harriet Hippo

Objectives

- The children will be able to demonstrate understanding of "opposites" by showing up and down movements.
- The children will discuss facts about a hippopotamus
- The children will identify the words Harriet Hippo from a group of similar words
- The children will log in a picture, sentence, or story, in their movement journals

Part 1

Read the song through as a story. Talk about what the hippo is doing in the story. Enact the movements Harriet Hippo is doing in the story. Discuss the importance of moving to stay healthy. Contrast healthy "moving" to unhealthy "sedentary" activities. Talk about the ramifications of an unhealthy lifestyle (disease, obesity, tiredness, laziness, etc).

Teach the song and the choreography

Harriet Hippo
(Twinkle Twinkle Little Star)

Harriet Hippo getting fit
Reach up, clap 2 times Reach down, clap 2 times

Reaching, stretching, don't you sit
Reach up, clap 2 times Reach down, clap 2 times

Jumping, Running, Steppin' in the groove
Jump twice, run, step up and down

Don't sit down you've got to move
Hands on knees, bend knees four times while shaking head "NO"

Harriet Hippo getting fit
Reach up, clap 2 times Reach down, clap 2 times

Reaching, stretching, don't you sit
Reach up, clap 2 times Reach down, clap 2 times

Repeat

Part 2

"Funominal" Facts

- Did you know that a "pig" is a distant relative of the hippo?
- Did you know that the hippo has an even number of toes?
    - Do you have an even number of toes on each foot?
    - How many toes do you have on each foot? 5
    - How many toes do you think a hippo has on each foot? 4
- Did you know that when a hippo opens his mouth, there are approximately four feet between the upper and lower teeth?
    - Compare the distance to the height of the children.
    - Most young children could stand in a hippo's month!
- Did you know hippos can stay underwater for 4-5 minutes?
    - Time it and compare to length of time humans can hold their breath.
- Hippo Talk
    - "I'm angry" - Deep roars and growls
    - "I'm excited" - Neigh sounds like a horse
    - "Fighting" - Squeal sound like a pig
    - "Just clearing my nose" - Snort
    - Have children make various hippo sounds
- Hippo Stats
    - Approximately 4-1/2 feet tall
    - Approximately 11-1/2 feet long
    - Approximately 4,000 lbs (2 tons)

Word Recognition

On index cards, write numerous "H" words, including the words Harriet and Hippo. (Harriest, hip, Harry, hippo, happy, etc). Mix the cards up in the middle of the floor, face down. Have the children scramble to find all the words that say "Harriet" and "Hippo".

Part 3

Talk and Tell

Harriet Hippo is getting fit.

LESSON PLAN
O'Iguana

Objectives

- The children will strengthen the muscles of their shoulders and arms
- The children will learn the difference between right and left
- The children will be able to name at least two facts about iguanas
- The children will identify the word iguana from a list of similar words

Part 1

Read the song as a story. Define the words: <u>Pumping</u> (as referred to in strengthening) <u>Flexing</u> (Bending) and the phrase, <u>Get In Shape</u>

Teach the Song and Choreography

O' Iguana (Clementine)
Using SPRI QuikFit

Begin with one end of the QuikFit in each hand. Right hand on right hip, Left hand on left hip. End with the working hand at the shoulder. Hold and slowly return to beginning position.

O Iguana
Left hand moves toward left shoulder

Pumping up,
Left hand moves toward left shoulder

Flexing muscles,
Left hand moves toward left shoulder

Let's get movin' don't be late
Run in place

Repeat
Repeat entire exercise sequence with right side

O Iguana
Left hand moves back to left hip

let's get in shape
Left hand moves back to left hip

move your body
Left hand moves back to left hip

✓ Checkpoints: Keep wrists straight
Avoid pulling up with back
Torso remains still
Keep shoulders down and relaxed

Part 2

About the Music

- Discuss the Reggae/Jamaican style of music used
- Using a map, point out where the children live, then point out the islands that generally have "reggae" as a part of their culture
- Play other songs that have a "reggae" rhythm and style
- Discuss the "Limbo" pole activity. Bring in a pole and try the limbo to this song

"Funominal" Facts

- Did you know that iguanas have powerful toenails which help it climb the large trees in the tropical lowlands?
- Did you know that iguanas can live in shrubs, but prefer to live in water?
- Did you know that many iguanas can run on their hind legs like the dinosaurs?
- Did you know that iguanas are a food delicacy in Mexico?
  (Kind of like lobster is in the United States)
- Did you know iguanas can be from 1 to 6 feet in length?

Iguana Riddle

What is iguana spelled backwards?   Anaugi (Ana/oo/gee)

Part 3
Talk and Tell

Iguana likes working his legs.

LESSON PLAN
Yakety Yak

Objectives

- The children will be able to strengthen their arm muscles by completing at least eight tricep exercises.
- The children will be able to name at least two synonyms and antonyms for the word "yakety"
- The children will be able to tell at least two facts about the Yak

Part 1

Read the lyrics to the song as a story
Discuss and teach the choreography

YAKETY YAK
(Polly Wolly Doddle)
Using SPRI Quikfit

Begin standing stop step facing short end of step, holding QuikFit in each hand

Oh I went to the gym to move about
Step off step to the right side, extend the tricep

Singing strengthen tighten tonin' all the day
Return to atop the step, squat 4 times

My heart gets strong and my muscles too
Step off step to the left side, extend the tricep to the left

Singing strengthen tighten tonin' all the day
Stand stop the step, squat 4 times

Yakety Yak, yakety yak
Cowboy straddle down, Jump up

Yakety Yak works out real hard
Cowboy straddle down, Jump up

For I'm gettin' energy
Step off step to the right, tricep extension to the right, return to atop the step

Yip e i Yip ee ee
Step off step to the left, tricep extension to the left, return to atop the step

Singing strengthen tighten tonin' all the day
Stand atop the step and squat 4 times

Part 2

"Funominal" Facts

- Did you know that the yak is sometimes called the "grunting ox"? Why do you think that is so?
- Did you know that the male yaks are called "bulls" and are nearly 6 feet tall and weigh 1200 pounds?
- Did you know that yaks are found only in the remote vastnesses of Tibet?
- Did you know that the yak has poor sight and hearing, but a very well developed sense of smell?

- Graph/chart the number of children who have seen a yak
- Name other animals that resemble a yak
- Name words that rhyme with yak, or start/end the same
- Make up silly sentences about a Yakety Yak
- Chart synonyms and antonyms of the word yakety (talkative)

Part 3

Talk and Tell

Yakety Yak strengthens his muscles.

Objectives

- The children will strengthen their abdominals by completing at least twelve curl ups
- The children will demonstrate proper execution and breathing of the curl ups
- The children will name at least three functions of their abdominals and backs
- The children will demonstrate an understanding of the voting system by nominating and voting for a name of the porcupine
- The children will tell the purpose/function of porcupine "needles"

Part 1

Read the lyrics as a story
Discuss the story
Teach the song and choreography

PORCUPINE IS LOOKING FINE
(Little Brown Jug)

Begin lying on back

My abs and back will help me be
Curl up (exhale) return to starting position

Happy and strong just wait you'll see
Curl up (exhale) return to starting position

Curl up, hold, then breathe it out
Oh what fun it's all about
Curl up, hold, return to starting position

Porcupine, porcupine, porcupine is looking fine
Porcupine, porcupine, porcupine is looking fine
Curl ups, clap 3 times/return to starting position, clap 3 times

---

Part 2

"Funominal" Facts

- Did you know the word porcupine originally meant a "pig with spines"?
- Did you know that when porcupines are annoyed or angry, they rattle the sharp quills (needles) on their tails and then run backward to attack their intruder?
- Did you know that porcupines never shoot their quills?
- Did you know that a porcupine weighs about 15 pounds?

Voting For A Name

- Conduct a class poll for names for the porcupine
- Choose the three favorite names and split the group into three "parties"
- Let the party leaders campaign to the other classes for their candidate's name
- Hold a grade level election with secret ballots, ballot boxes, election judges, tally counters, etc.
- This activity can be as elaborate as you choose. You can always generate a one page newsletter announcing the results of the vote, etc.

Part 3

Talk and Tell

P p

Porcupine is looking fine.

Objectives

• The children will be able to participate in non-stop movement to the entire song
• The children will be able to name at least two synonyms for the word lazy
• The children will be able to name at least two antonyms for the word lazy
• The children will be able to name at least three lazy behaviors
• The children will be able to name at least three non-lazy behaviors

Part 1

Read lyrics of song as a story
Discuss
Teach movements

LAZY WALRUS
(Lazy Mary)

Lazy walrus will you step up?
Will you step up?
Will you step up?
Double Step

Lazy Walrus will you step up?
Will you step up today?
Double Step

No, no children I won't step up
I won't step up
I won't step up
Double Step, shake heads "no" (opposite lead leg)

No, no children I won't step up
I won't step up today.
Double Step, shake heads "no"

Lazy Walrus step with us please
Step with us please
Step with us please
Victory Step (see terminology)

Lazy Walrus step with us please
Step with us please today
Skip around steps

OK children we all will step
We all will step
We all will step
Victory Step (opposite lead leg)

OK children we all will step
We'll step today hey hey.
Skip around step

Part 2

"Funominal" Facts

- Did you know the walrus uses its long tusks to dig for food?
- Did you know that the walrus spends his life living on ice, in the bitter cold and fierce blizzards?
- Did you know the walrus' tusks are made of ivory?
- The large male walrus' can measure up to 11 feet long and weigh between 2000 and 3000 pounds.
- The walrus is a slow, clumsy swimmer, but because of its size can usually protect itself from enemies.

- Use a map to find the arctic areas where walrus' live
- Chart lazy vs. non lazy animal behaviors. Compare to lazy/non-lazy human behaviors.
- Discuss other words that mean lazy
- Discuss opposite of lazy
- Discuss what lazy behaviors the children engage in

Part 3

Talk and Tell

Lazy Walrus step with us please.

Objectives

- The children will be able to classify animals into mammals, reptiles, fish, etc.
- The children will be able to name at least two characteristics of all mammals
- The children will be able to name at least two characteristics of all reptiles
- The children will be able to name at least two characteristics of all fish
- The children will be able to participate in non-stop movements for the entire song
- The children will be able to dramatize animal movements in the song
- The children will be able to name at least two facts about the lion, monkey, and snake

Part 1

Read lyrics of song as a story
Discuss
Teach movements

ANIMAL STEP
(Mulberry Bush)

This is the way the lion steps
The lion steps, the lion steps
This is the way the lion steps
Up, up, roar, roar, down, down.
Double Step with "clawing" actions with hands. Children "ROAR" during last line of this verse

REPEAT ABOVE
Double Step with opposite leg leading

This is the way the monkey steps
The monkey steps
The monkey steps
This is the way the monkey steps
Up kick ee ee down tap
Step N Karate Kick move (see terminology) with monkey "scratching" actions with hands. Children "EEEEEE" during last line of this verse

REPEAT MONKEY VERSE
Step N Karate Kick with opposite lead leg

This is the way the Snake will step
The snake will step
The snake will step
This is the way the snake will step
Up Up S-S- down down
Victory Step, hands together modeling slithering action of a snakes body

REPEAT ABOVE VERSE WITH . . . Quail (Tweet Tweet)
Victory Step with opposite leg

This is the way the children step
The children step
The children step
This is the way the children step
Up down and all around
Alternating Up N Karate Kick
On last line, children walk around their steps

REPEAT CHILDREN VERSE

Part 2

"Funominal" Facts

LION
• Did you know that the lion's nickname has been "King of the Beasts"?
• Did you know that baby lions are called "cubs"?
• A boy lion may weigh around 500 pounds and a girl about 300 pounds
• A lion rarely roars his/her ferocious roar during the daylight hours.
Every evening after sunset and throughout the night you can hear the
lion's loud ROAR.

SNAKE
• Did you know that there are about 3000 different kinds of snakes?
• Did you know that most snakes are shy and won't harm you unless you bother them?
• Did you know that snakes smell and taste by flicking their tongues in and
  out? Can you imitate a snake?
• Did you know that the longest non-poisonous snake is the Anaconda?
  It is around 37 feet long. Measure how long that is out in the hallway.
• Did you know that the shortest snake in the Thread snake?
  It is only 4-1/2 inches long. Measure that.

MONKEY
• Did you know that a group of monkeys is called a "troop"?
• Monkeys are found in the tropical and semitropical areas of Africa, Asia, Central
  and South America.
• Some monkeys cram their mouths with food, storing it in their cheek pouches.
  Then they run off to a safe place to chew at their leisure. Do you know other
  animals who store their food in their mouth pouches?

• Chart and classify all animals learned so far into mammal, fish, reptile
• Discuss characteristics of each classification
• Compare and contrast animals
• Draw conclusions

Suppplemental Activities
Fun Games
• Animal Charades

Using the animals of the songs we've already learned, children enact animals while the class tries to guess what animal they are acting out. The entire class acts like the animal being acted out.
(ex. Lion - roaring, Walrus - sleeping, Snake - slithering)

• Animal Partner
• Split class into 2 groups
• Group 1 goes into hall
• Group 2 stays in class
• Assign each child in Group 1 an animal that makes a distinguishing sound (i.e. cow, horse, lion)
• Assign the same animals to the children in group B
• Both groups A and B are in the classroom. Nobody tells what animal they are.
• Blindfold the children, clear the area of all obstacles
• When given the cue, all children from groups A and B start making their animal sounds as they move about the area looking for their brother/sister animal whose making the same sound as they are.
(NOTE: Make sure same sound is used by both animals in group A and B (i.e. both cows say moo-moo)
• Game ends when all children are standing next to their animal partner

Part 3
Talk and Tell

The Lion goes Roar, Roar.

The Monkey goes EE.

The Snake goes S-S.

The Quail goes Tweet Tweet.

LESSON PLAN
1 Little 2 Little Animal Workout

Objectives

- The children will be able to point to different muscles of their body
- The children will be able to identify a turtle, vulture, newt
- The children will be able to complete at least six pushups with good form and alignment
- The children will be able to complete at least 8 lunges on alternating legs with good form and alignment
- The children will be able to categorize animals into appropriate classifications; bird, reptile, mammal, amphibian
- The children will be able to name at least one fact about each animal in this song

Part 1

Read lyrics of song as a story
Discuss the story
Teach the song and choreography

ONE LITTLE, TWO LITTLE ANIMAL WORK OUT
(10 Little Indians)

Chorus:
1 little 2 little 3 little muscles
4 little 5 little 6 little muscles
7 little 8 little 9 little muscles
Children jump into the air on each number

Working out today
Clap hands

Turtle likes to pushup 1-2-3
Turtle likes to pushup 1-2-3
Turtle likes to pushup 1-2-3
Children do modified pushups

Working out today
Clap hands and stand up

Repeat Chorus

Vulture likes to lunge right 1-2-3
Vulture likes to lunge right 1-2-3
Vulture likes to lunge right 1-2-3
Children lunge right with arms outstretched as "vulture" wings

Working out today
Clap hands and hop in place

Repeat Chorus

Newt likes to lunge left 1-2-3
Newt likes to lunge left 1-2-3
Newt likes to lunge left 1-2-3
Children lunge left

Working out today
Clap hands and hop in place

Repeat Chorus

Part 2

"Funominal" Facts

NEWT
- Did you know that a newt is an amphibian with a tail?
- The newt lives a "triple" life. It is born in the water, then it lives on the land for two or three years? Finally, in adulthood, it returns to the water to live out the remainder of its life.
- The newts' relative is the salamander.

TURTLE
- Did you know turtles have been around for 200 million years? Longer than humans have.
- If a turtle has a "high-domed" shell, it lives on the land, freshwater and sea turtles have flat shells.
- Turtles don't have teeth, rather, they have a horny beak like bird. The beak helps them tear and crush their food.
- Turtles like to eat flowers, grass, vegetables, fruit, and yes, dog food!!
- Turtles don't sweat, therefore, to cool off, they bury themselves in the dirt or sand near water or hide in a shady area.

VULTURE
- Did you know the vulture is a member of the falcon family?
- The king vulture of tropical America is the most colorful.
- Vultures feed on other creatures and any garbage available.
- Although vultures are predators and eat other animals, they are beautiful when they glide through the air.
- Vultures like to soar in wide open circles high in the sky.

Supplemental Activity

Animal Fish Game

Get three large posterboards. Place one of these words on each poster: Bird, Reptile, Mammal, Amphibian. Cut out pictures of animals and place them in a bucket. Have children reach in bucket and pull out picture of animal. They place the animal on the appropriate posterboard.
(Eagle/Vulture = birds)

Part 3

Talk and Tell

The Turtle likes to workout.

The Vulture likes to step up.

The Nutty Newt works out today.

Objectives

- The children will be able to point to their biceps muscles
- The children will be able to point to their triceps muscles
- The children will be able to point to their hamstrings and quadriceps muscles
- The children will be able to point to their gluteus maximus and abdominal muscles
- The children will be able to point to their lattisimus dorsi and deltoid muscles
- The children will be able to point to their trapezius and pectoralis muscles
- The children will be able to point to their back muscles
- The children will be able to list at least three facts about a unicorn
- The children will be able to demonstrate the joint action for each muscle represented in this song

Part 1

Read the lyrics of the song as a story
Teach the song and choreography

Muscle Identification:

Muscle	Location	Action
Biceps	front of the arm	bend elbow
Triceps	back of the arm	extends elbow
Lats	sides of the back	pulls arms down
Delts	top of shoulders	pushes arms up
Traps	upper back	pulls arms back
Pecs	chest muscles	pushes arms front/across chest
Hamstrings	back upper thigh	bend knees
Quadriceps	front upper thigh	extends knees
Abdominals	front of the torso	bends torso at the waist
Back	back of the torso	extends torso at the waist

UNICORN PUMP
(Alouette)

Unicorn is pumping up her body
Unicorn pumps up all day
Unicorn is pumping up her body
Unicorn pumps up all day
Children march around in a circle with hand simulating a unicorn's horn on top of head during lines 1 and 3
Children make muscles with arms on lines 2 and 4

Biceps Triceps Hamstrings too
Quads and Gluts Abdominals Whew
Point to each muscle. On "Whew", wipe brow

Unicorn, Unicorn, Pump it up Pump it up . . . Oh
Clap three times   Pump muscles

On each part below, the instructor does the first action, the children repeat it the second time
**Biceps bend, Biceps bend/Tri's extend Tri's extend
**Lats pull down, Lats pull down/Delts push up, Delts push up
**Traps pull back, Traps pull back/Pecs push front, Pecs push front
**Hams bend knees, Hams bend knees/Quads extend, quads extend
**Abs bend front Abs bend front/Back stands up, Back stands up

Note: Each time through, you sing the next ** line. Repeat the previous line and add on the new line.

Part 2
"Funominal" Facts
- Did you know that a unicorn is a "mythical" creature?
- Name other "mythical" creatures. Trolls, witches, goblins, sphinx
- A unicorn is usually seen as a large horse with a single horn on its forehead
- It is said that the unicorn is a combination of an antelope (hind legs), lion (tail), and goat (beard)

Supplemental Activities
M&M Tag (Muscle and Movement Tag)
- Pair the children
- Make tags to identify muscles
- Make tags to identify movements of muscles
- Place all the tags in a baggie. Give a baggie to each team
- Give each team a roll of tape
- Each pair of children will decide who will be the M&M Tagger.
    The "tagger" will tape all the tags on their partners in the correct location.
    (Ex. biceps tag, and bend the elbow tag, will both be taped on the front
    of the child's arm)
- When the whistle is blown, all taggers will begin taping the muscles, and
    the muscle movements on their partners. The partners can assist their
    taggers. The object is to get all the tags in the correct location.

Part 3
Talk and Tell

The Unicorn steps to the beat.

LESSON PLAN
Octopus Step

Objectives

- The children will be able to tell at least three octopus facts
- The children will be able to identify the parts of their bodies listed in the song
- The children will be able to do the "hokey pokey" as sung in this song
- The children will be able to distinguish left from right
- The children will be able to name at least five words that contain the short "o" sound as in octopus

Part 1

Read the lyrics of the song as a story
Teach the lyrics and movements of the song

OCTOPUS STEP
(Hokey Pokey)

You put your right foot up
Tap right foot onto step

You put your left foot up
Tap left foot onto step

You put your right foot up
Tap right foot onto step

And you twist it all about
With foot atop step, twist

Chorus:
You do the Octopus Step
Having fun up up down down
Basic Step

Twistin it all about
Twist while standing on floor

Do as verse directs
Verses:
  2nd - right knee up/left knee up
  3rd - right heel back/left heel back
  4th - right thigh out/left thigh out

Part 2

"Funominal" Facts

- An octopus is considered an invertebrate. It has no backbone or spine.
    - Are you an invertebrate? Why
- Humans are considered vertebrates. What do you think this term means?
- Octopus' have 8 arms called tentacles
- Some octopus that live in the Pacific Ocean have arms that are 16 feet long
    - Find the Pacific Ocean on the map. Measure 16 feet in length.
- The octopus doesn't have shells or fins
- The octopus can change colors quickly to blend in with their background to hide from their enemies.
- When the octopus gets into trouble, he shoots a brown or black ink-like fluid at his enemies, so he can escape.
- The octopus moves by crawling. They use the "Suckers" on their arms to pull themselves along

Supplemental Activities

- Name at least 5 other words that have a short "o" sound as in octopus.
    - Mop, Fox, Robber, Rock, Mom
- Using yarn and semi-round styrofoam balls, make a class octopus and give him/her a name. (To make semi-round ball, cut round styrofoam ball in half) Using 34" strings of yarn, glue yarn atop styrofoam ball until its fully covered. Allow the excess yarn to hang. Once the ball has been covered, separate the excess yarn into eight sections. Braid or twist each section to form tentacles. (Pairs of children can be responsible for each tentacle) Rubber band the end of each tentacle to hold the braid or twist in place. Glue two eyes on the front of the ball.

Part 3

Talk and Tell

Let's do the Octopus step.

Objectives

- The children will be able to identify the parts of their bodies referred to in this song
- The children will be able to tell at least three facts about a bear
- The children will be able to do all the activities referred to in the song
- The children will be able to name at least three other words rhyming with bear

Part 1

Read the lyrics of the song as a story
Teach the song and choreography

BEEBOP BEAR
(Happy and You Know It)
Using SPRI QuikFit

If you're movin' gettin' fit pump your arms, pump pump
March forward while pumping your biceps (bending arms)

If you're movin' gettin' fit pump your arms, pump pump
March backward while pumping your biceps

If you're movin' gettin' fit work your body you've got it
March in a circle pumping your biceps

If your movin' gettin' fit pump your arms, pump, pump
Touch your knees twice, clap your hands twice, pump your biceps twice

Do as verse directs
Verse Numbers
2. Extend your arms, extend, extend
3. Shrug your shoulders, shrug, shrug
4. Squeeze your pecs, squeeze, squeeze
5. Arms pull down, pull down
6. Arms push up, push up
7. Bend your knee, bend, bend
8. Straighten your knee, straighten, straighten

Part 2

"Funominal" Facts

- The male bear is called a boar.
- The female bear is called a sow
- The bear's claws are longer on the front feet than the back feet
- The claws are as long as a child's hand
- Bears are "pigeon-toed". Their front feet turn in. Try walking like a bear. When they walk, their front and back legs on the same side move forward together.
- The polar bears can be 8-9 feet tall and weigh up to 1500 pounds
- The baby bear is called a cub

Supplemental Activities

- Name other words that rhyme with bear.
- Bee, Ball, Bounce
    - Bounce ball to a partner and say a "B" word

Part 3

Talk and Tell

BeeBop Bear pumps up his muscles.

Objectives

- The children will be able to complete the movements in the song
- The children will be able to use "sign" language to sign the letters in the word zebra
- The children will be able to name at least three zebra facts
- The children will be able to identify pictures and objects that begin with the letter Z

Part 1

Read the lyrics of the song as a story
Discuss the song
Teach the song and choreography

SignLanguage

Z	=	with index finger make "z" in air
E	=	close fist with thumb on third and fourth fingernail
B	=	four fingers together pointing upward, thumb touching palm
R	=	two fingers together pointing upward, other three fingers in palm
A	=	close fist, thumb next to index finger pointing upward

Z • E • B • R • A
(Bingo)

There was a keeper who had a pet
Clap hands as marching around the step

And wanted him to move-o
Children move their entire body

Z-E-B-R-A   Z-E-B-R-A   Z-E-B-R-A
Sign Language Spells Out Letters Z E B R A

Oh Zebra won't you move now
Tap right foot atop step, tap left foot atop the step

.

The Zebra looked at him in aw
March atop step, hands at eyeballs

And said no I won't move now
March on floor, shaking head no

Z-E-B-R-A   Z-E-B-R-A   Z-E-B-R-A
Sign Language Spells Out Letters Z E B R A

Oh Zebra won't you move now
Tap right foot atop the step, tap left foot atop the step

One day the keeper played this game
Clap hands as marching around the step

It goes something like this
Hop in place behind step
Up up wiggle your hips
Stand atop step and wiggle hips

Down Down move your lips
Step to floor and move lips

Walk around and skip, skip, skip
Walk around step and skip

On zebra won't you move now
Clap hands

•

The Zebra thought this might be fun
Walk around step clapping hands

He said OK I'll try it
March behind step, hands making "OK" sign

Up up wiggle your hips
Stand atop step and wiggle hips

Down down move your lips
Step down, march on floor, move lips

Walk around and skip skip skip
Walk around step and skip

The Zebra likes to move now
Move entire body

Part 2

"Funominal" Facts

- Zebras are abundant on the plains of Africa.
- The zebra's stripes are very important for camouflage - for blending in with the tall grass.
- When the zebra's are all in a group, it is difficult to tell where one zebra begins and where the other one ends. It drives a predator "batty".
- The zebra stripes are unique to each zebra. His/her stripes are like his/her fingerprints. Lead into class fingerprint discussion. Let children contrast and compare their fingerprints using a ink pad and white paper.
- Zebra's can run up to 60 miles an hour.

Supplemental Activities

- Make a zig zag zebra art design. Using white paper and black paint or crayons, make zig zag patterns. Use fat, thin, straight, squiggly lines to create unique patterns.
- Discuss "sign language". Get a book on signing from the library. Teach children the letters of the alphabet. Let them try to spell their name.
- Pin the "Z" on the zebra.

    Outline a large zebra on butcher paper. Affix to a wall. Children cut out pictures that begin with the letter Z. Place small piece of tape on each picture. Blindfold the children. Spin them around one at a time and point them in the direction of the zebra. The goal is to have them tape their Z picture in the zebra shape.

Part 3

Talk and Tell

The Zebra likes to move now.

LESSON PLAN
Allie-gator

Objectives
- The children will be able to demonstrate the "A" step
- The children will be able to name at least three alligator facts
- The children will be able to successfully complete the movements of this song

Part 1
Read lyrics of song as a story
Teach the song and choreography

ALLIE-GATOR
(Are You Sleeping)

A-Alligator A-Alligator
See me step
See me step
A Step

Working out is fun now
When you feel the rhythm
March on floor clap hands, slap legs

Up, up, down, tap
Basic step, tap down

Up, up, down, tap
Basic step, tap down

Part 2
"Funominal" Facts
- Alligators are the largest reptiles in the world.
- Alligators have at least 60 sharp teeth.
- Alligators have a flat, broad head. Crocodiles have a long, triangle shaped head.
- When alligators get angry, they hiss, snap their jaws, and flap their tails.

Part 3
Talk and Tell

Allie the Alligator feels the rhythm.

Objectives

- The children will be able to tell at least three rabbit facts
- The children will be able to play the "bunny hop" game
- The children will be able to successfully complete the moves for this song
- The children will be able to play the "carrot tag" game

Part 1

Read the lyrics of the song as a story
Teach the lyrics and movements of the song

RABBIT STEP UP
(Row Row Row Your Boat)

R-R- Rabbit Step
Stepping up and down
When you get back to the ground
Basic step, hands on head like "bunny ears"

Just hop yourself around
Hop around on floor

Repeat
Basic Step with opposite lead leg

Part 2

"Funominal" Facts

- Rabbits hop like another animal we've learned about. Which one? Kangaroo
- Rabbits rear feet are much bigger than their forefeet.
- Can you hop like a rabbit?
- Do any of you have a rabbit for a pet?
- Rabbits like to eat carrots, corn kernels, and alfalfa.
- Read the story "PETER COTTONTAIL"
- Play "Bunny Hop" music and make a bunny hop line

Supplemental Activity

Carrot Tag Game

Cut out orange carrots (from construction paper). Affix to a cloth belt. Children wear belts with carrots hanging. The object of the game is to hop around and try to tag the other rabbits' carrots. When tagged, the child hooks on. Now the "line" hops together to continue tagging rabbits. Eventually, the entire group will be in one line, once everyone gets tagged, dance to the Bunny Hop song.

Part 3
Talk and Tell

The Rabbit likes to hop and step.

Objectives

- The children will be able to recognize the "blues" style of music
- The children will be able to complete the movements of the song
- The children will be able to name at least three kinds of cats
- The children will be able to name at least three cat facts

Part 1

Read the lyrics of the song as a story
Teach the lyrics and movements of the song

KITTY CAT SIT STEP
(I'm a Little Teapot)

*Turn Step

Kitty Kitty Cat Tap 1-2-3
2 Tap Ups to right corner

Sitting on my step so happily
2 Tap Ups to left corner

When I see a mouse I want to hop
2 Tap Ups to right corner

Right on him and over the top
Jump in place, move across the top

Repeat
Same choreography except on opposite side of step

Part 2

"Funominal" Facts

- Cats have been around for more than 50 million years.
- Lions, tigers, leopards, and jaguars are members of the "big cat" group.
- Big cats eat lying down; little cats eat in a crouched position.
- Big cats purr only when breathing out; little cats can purr continuously while breathing in and out.
- Big cats have loud roars; little cats have high pitched screams.
- All cats walk on their toes. Can you walk on your toes?
- Cats love to stretch. Can you stretch like a cat?

Supplemental Activities

- Cut out pictures of different kinds of cats
- Chart the number of children who own cats
- Compare boys/girls
- Chart and compare other pets children have. Draw conclusions

Part 3

Talk and Tell

Kitty Cat taps his step.

LESSON PLAN
Danny Dig Dog

Objectives

- The children will be able to name at least three facts about dogs
- The children will be able to name at least three different types of dogs
- The children will make "Dog Bone" treats
- The children will listen to the story or video 101 Dalmatians
- The children will play "Doggie Doggie Where's My Bone"

Part 1

Read the lyrics of the song as a story
Teach the song and movements

DANNY DIG DOG
(London Bridge)

Danny Dig Dog turn around
Turn around, turn around
Danny Dig Dog turn around
Turn around in one place or Turn step

Up and over
Move across the top

Tap your feet up 1-2-3
1-2-3   1-2-3
Tap your feet up 1-2-3
Tap right and left toes atop the step

Up and over
Move across the top

Danny Dig Dog turn around
Turn around, turn around
Danny Dig Dog turn around
Turn around in place or Turn step

Up and over
Move across the top

Repeat

Part 2

"Funominal" Facts

- There are two types of dogs: domestic and wild
- Some wild dogs are the coyote, jackal, and fox
- Some domestic dogs are the poodle, boxer, great dane, german sheppard,
  terrier, dalmatian
- The baby wild dog is called a cub
- The baby domestic dog is called a puppy

Supplemental Activities

Making "Dog Bones"

Ingredients:
      Crushed graham crackers
      Powdered dry milk (comes in a box)
      Honey
      Peanut Butter
      Wax Paper

Recipe:
1. After washing hands, place crushed graham crackers in a large bowl
2. Mix in peanut butter, honey, and dry milk until mixture becomes firm
3. Work in more graham crackers until consistency is dough-like
4. Using a hand-ful of dough, let children shape their own dog bone.
   To do this, roll into a log shape, then flatten. Pinch and shape the edges to form a dog bone shape
5. Set it on a piece of wax paper. Sprinkle with graham crackers. Chill for 30 minutes

- Read story or watch video of "101 Dalmatians"
- Play "Doggie Doggie Where's My Bone". Select one child to be the doggie. The "doggie" sits in a chair, eyes closed, with a "bone" (eraser or ball) underneath. Select another child to take the bone from under the chair and hide it. The "doggie" opens their eyes and searches for the bone. The class says "Doggie Doggie, where's my bone, somebody took it and ran right home".
- Children bring in pictures of various types of domestic dogs. Have them tell about the dog they selected. Make a posterboard entitled "Doggin' It".

Part 3
Talk and Tell

64

Danny Dig Dog steps up and down.

Objectives

- The children will be able to complete the moves of this song
- The children will be able to name at least three elephant facts
- The children will be able to do the "Baby Elephant Walk"
- The children will listen to, read, or watch "Dumbo"

Part 1

Read the lyrics of the song as a story
Teach the song and movements

EL-E-Phant
(Three Blind Mice)

El-e-phant   El-e-phant
March with feet wide apart

See how he steps
Victory Step

See how he steps
Victory Step

He steps atop with all his might
March atop the step

He leaps in the air just see his height
Stand on tip toes and reach to ceiling

Now down again, he's out of sight
March on floor

Oh El-e-phant
Wide march on floor

Repeat

Part 2

"Funominal" Facts

- The elephant is the largest living land animal
- The elephant is taller than the ceiling in your home and weighs more than 100 5th graders all together.
- Many mean hunters kill African elephants for their tusks, which are made of ivory. If we don't help save these creatures, they may become extinct. Discuss the term extinct. Give examples of animals that are extinct as well as those that are endangered.
- African elephants have big floppy ears. The Asian elephants have small ears.

- Elephants walk on their toes. Can you walk on your toes? Try it.
- The elephant trunk is actually a long upper lip and nose combined. Elephants breathe mostly through their trunks.
- If you invited an elephant to dinner, here's what you'd need to feed him/her.
  To feed one elephant for a year, you'll need:
    50,000 pounds of hay
    15,000 pounds of dry alfalfa
    1,000 pounds of rolled oats
    30,000 pounds of carrots, cabbage, lettuce, and apples
    16,000 gallons of water
- An elephant spends 18 hours a day eating 600 pounds of food. WOW!
- To talk to each other, the elephants purr, grunt, trumpet, and scream. Try to make elephant soundss.
- An elephant weighs around 5 tons
- If an elephant gets sick and has a fever, the animal doctor gives him/her 100 aspirins three times a day and hoses him/her with cold water to reduce his/her fever.

Supplemental Activities

- Read book or watch video entitled "Dumbo"
- Play the song "Baby Elephant Walk". Do the elephant walk around the room.
  Make noises like the elephants do.
- Elephant Food Sampling Day:
  - Bring in samples of alfalfa, carrots, cabbage, apples, rolled oats, and lettuce
  - Have children taste each
  - Chart the children's most favorite elephant food
  - Chart the children's least favorite elephant food
  - Compare/contrast/draw conclusions

Part 3
Talk and Tell

Ellie the Elephant leaps up with all his might.

Objectives

- The children will be able to identify all the muscles listed in the song
- The children will be able to name at least three fox facts
- The children will be able to do the Funky Fox Trot activity for at least 5 minutes without stopping

Part 1

Read the lyrics of the song as a story
Discuss the song
Teach the song and movements

FUNKY FANNY FOX
(Eensy Weensy Spider)
Using SPRI QuikFit

Sit on step with a partner; children act out song

On, Funky Fanny Fox was sitting all alone
Working on her biceps, moan, moan, moan
Out popped her friend and joined in her workout
And Funky Fanny Fox no longer pouts

Verses:

2. Triceps
3. Deltoids
4. Hamstrings
5. Quads

Part 2

"Funominal" Facts
- Did you know that a fox is a member of the wild dog family?
- Baby foxes are called cubs
- A fox can run as fast as 45 miles an hour
- A fox weighs between 5-10 pounds. Find other things that weigh between 5-10 pounds. Chart the children's birth weights. Compare/contrast/draw conclusions.

Supplemental Activities
Funky Fox Trot - needed one towel per child
Standing on the towel with bare feet, explore as many different ways to move the towel without putting feet on the floor. Now try to sit on the towel. Try twisting, sliding, scissoring, spinning, etc. Try moving like a sly fox. Play "fox trot" music.

Part 3
Talk and Tell

Ff

Funky Fanny Fox works on her muscles.

Objectives

- The children will be able to name at least three gorilla facts
- The children will be able to make "Gorilla Treats"
- The children will be able to complete the gorilla movements in the song
- The children will be able to do the "Knuckle Walk"

Part 1

Read the lyrics of the song as a story
Teach the song and movements

GOLLY GORILLA STEP
(Farmer In The Dell)

Gorilla on a step
Gorilla on a step
Heigh Ho gorilla man
Gorilla on a step
March atop the step, children "pounding" chest as a gorilla
March on the floor, children "pounding" chest as a gorilla

He's tapping up and down
He's tapping up and down
Heigh Ho gorilla man
He's tapping up and down
Tap up and down

He's walking all around
He's walking all around
Heigh ho gorilla man
He's walking all around
Walk around step

Repeat
Repeat Choreography with other lead leg

Part 2

"Funominal" Facts

- There are three types of gorillas in Africa:
  - The Western Lowland (from West Africa)
  - The Eastern Lowland (from central Africa rainforests)
  - The Mountain gorillas
- Did you know that an adult gorilla is VERY strong. The adult male gorilla could lift FIVE lions!!
- Gorillas are a lot like us. They have five fingers, fingernails, and fingerprints
  90% of gorillas are right-handed. Are you right-handed or left-handed?
  Chart/compare/contrast/draw conclusions of "handedness" in the class.

- The gorilla "knuckle-walks". Try walking like a gorilla. How does it feel?
- Gorillas eat between 30-40 pounds of food per day. Find out how much 30-40 pounds is. Weigh yourself/objects/food/etc. to compare.

Supplemental Activities

Making Gorilla Treats:

Ingredients:
    1/2 banana per child
    Creamy Peanut Butter
    Crushed nuts
    Popsicle Stick (1 per child)

Recipe:
1. After washing your hands, insert one popsicle stick into the back end of the 1/2 banana
2. Gently spread the peanut butter over the banana
3. Roll the peanut butter covered banana into a bowl of crushed peanuts
4. Eat it!!!

Part 3
Talk and Tell

Golly Gorilla gets stronger every day.

LESSON PLAN
Katie Kangaroo

Objectives

- The children will participate in non-stop activities for the entire duration of the song
- The children will tell at least three facts about their heart and what effect movement has on strengthening their heart
- The children will name at least four rhyming words in the song

Part 1

Read lyrics as a story
Discuss the story
Identify the rhyming words in the song
Teach the movements (if you are not using the step, do all the movements on the floor)

KATIE KANGAROO IS HAPPY
(I've Been Working on the Railroad)

Katie Kangaroo is happy
Double Step (see terminology explanations)

Working out today
Double Step

Katie Kangaroo is happy
Double Step

Join in don't go away
Double Step

Don't you feel your muscles moving
Basic Step

Get up have some fun
Jump in Air 4 times (standing on floor)

Don't you feel your heart is pumping
Basic Step

Ready set let's run
Run to another child's step so two children are at end's of step

Katie Kangaroo   Katie Kangaroo   Katie Kangaroo
Up N Karate Kick

Will step with you
Hop On Floor (changing lead legs for Karate Kick)

Katie Kangaroo   Katie Kangaroo
Up N Karate Kick

Katie Kangaroo and you
Hop On Floor (changing lead legs)

Look who's steppin with Katie
Basic Step

It's someone I knooooooooow
March on floor pointing to partner (change lead legs)

Look who's steppin with Katie
Basic Step (new lead leg)

Ready set let's go
Run back to their own step

Fe Fi Fiddle e i o
Double Step (pretend to play instruments)

Fee Fi Fiddle e i OOOO
Stand on floor (playing imaginary instruments)

Fe Fi Fiddle e i o
Double Step (new lead leg)

Ready Set Let's Go
Stand on floor (playing imaginary instruments)

Repeat

Part 2

"Funominal" Facts
- Did you know that a kangaroo is the largest living marsupial?
- A marsupial is an animal with a pouch
- Did you know that male kangaroos are called "boomers, and females are called "does"?
- Did you know that a group of kangaroos are called a "mob"?
- Did you know that a baby kangaroo is called a "joey"?
- Only the female kangaroos have a pouch
- Try the kangaroo walk . . . The kangaroo pushes its body forward with its hind legs, then puts down its front legs and tail, then swings both hind legs forward.
- Kangaroos weigh around 200 pounds and are between 5-7 feet tall
- Some kangaroos can jump 40 feet at 40 miles an hour!!

- Use a map and find Australia and Tasmania. Discuss these places as the homes of kangaroos
- Teach some Australian "lingo" (i.e. G-day = good day or hello)
- Compare kangaroos to the other animals we've learned about
- Discuss the heart, its importance, how to keep it healthy, etc.
- Have children find their heart beat (pulse), by placing their palm on the center of their chest
- Have children jump up and down for 30 seconds, and find their heart beat again.
   Discuss what happened

Part 3

Talk and Tell

Katie Kangaroo is happy.

Objectives

• The children will be able to jump from side to side using both feet simultaneously
• The children will be able to step atop the step Repetitively using good balance and execution

Part 1

Read the song as a story. Define the following terms: Quads (Quadriceps = the muscles on the front of your legs, responsible for straightening your knees from a bent position) Gluets (Gluteus Maximus = Buttocks Muscles, responsible for kicking your leg behind you and helping you walk upstairs)

Teach the Song and Choreography

JUMPING JAGUAR
(Baa Baa Black Sheep)

Jumping	Jaguar	can't you see
2 jumps to the right	*2 jumps to the left*	*stand in place, hands point to eyes twice*

It's as	easy as	1-2-3
Jump with feet apart twice	*Jump with feet together*	*Hop around*

Step with your quads
Step atop the step

And reach to the sky
Standing atop the step, reach to sky on tiptoes

Down with your gluets
Step down off the step

Oh me, Oh my
4 claps

Jumping Jaguar can't you see
Repeat moves from beginning

It's as easy as 1-2-3
Repeat moves from beginning

Repeat

Part 2

"Funominal" Facts
- Did you know a jaguar may be up to 6 or 8 feet long?
- Did you know a jaguar can weigh up to 250 pounds?
- Did you know that a jaguar is a good swimmer?
- Did you know that jaguars are found mainly in South and Central America as well as in Texas, New Mexico, and Arizona? Can you find these places on the map?
- Did you know the jaguar is a big cat? It's babies are called kittens.

Supplemental Activities
- Think of 10 other words that start with a "J" sound like Jaguar (i.e. Jump, Jill, Jelly)
- List at least five other activities a jaguar does that you also do (i.e. leap, run, walk eat, breathe)
- Name two things you do that a jaguar doesn't do (i.e. talk, skateboard)
- Have a Jumping Jubilee (For 1 minute, the entire group, jumps on 1 foot, two feet, with eyes closed, in a circle, etc)
- Name at least three other animals that are like a jaguar. (tiger, lion, leopard) Tell how these animals are alike and different than a jaguar.

Jumping Jaguar steps with ease.

Objectives

- The children will be able to identify their pectoral muscles that help them swim
- The children will be able to identify at least three parts of a fish
- The children will safely execute the exercises for this song
- The children will be able to name at least three types of fish

Part 1

Read the lyrics of the song as a story
Teach the rap and accompanying actions
Discuss parts of a fish (pectoral fin, dorsal fin, gills, etc)
Talk about and bring in pictures of various fish (goldfish, etc)

Teach the song and the choreography

FISH FISH XRAY FISH
(Baa Baa Black Sheep)
Using SPRI QuikFit

Fish Fish Xray Fish
One arm Pectoralis press (see terminology)

Swimming all around
Moves arms as if swimming

Working your pecs
One arm Pectoralis press

Don't touch the ground
Pectoralis press

Push a little, pull
Other arm, pectoralis press

And swim, swim, swim
Arms swim

Exhale, inhale, use your fin
Pectoralis press

Repeat

Part 2

"Funominal" Facts

- Did you know that an XRay fish is a tropical fish?
- Did you know that an XRay fish swims in a jerky fashion?
- Did you know that the boy XRay fish is smaller than the girl XRay fish?
- Did you know that the XRay fish is a shy fish?

Supplemental Activities

Bring in XRay

Talk about what an XRay is, if anyone in class has ever had XRays, etc.

Graph/Chart number of children who had XRays versus those who have not

Compare boys to girls

Discuss the following topics: bones/fractures/muscles/tendons

    Bones - support structure of body

    Fracture - A split in a bone

    Muscles - Pull on bones to make them move

    Tendons - Connect muscles to bones

Part 3

Talk and Tell

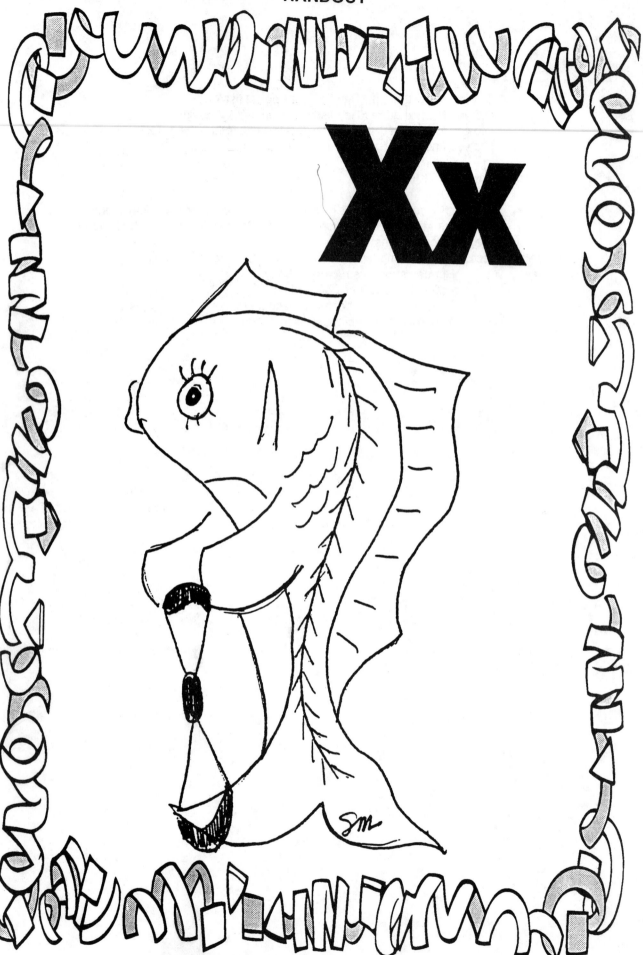

Xx

Xray Fish works her pecs.

KidZ Step Group Class Choreography

LEVEL 2 (ages 10-12)

Note: To empower the children and to give them an active role in the learning process, select children to assist teaching the class. They are responsible for coaching their peers, correcting alignments, etc.

*T*EACHING TECHNIQUE: Do not refer to right and left as RIGHT AND LEFT. This causes confusion. You and your child assistants will actually be mirroring the image of those children facing you. INSTEAD, find "environmental" markers to use as points of reference (i.e. windows, doors, clock, etc.) For example: When executing the Basic Step with a right leg lead, where the right leg is near the windows, say "Beginning with your foot closest to the windows, we'll do a Basic Step".

*M*USIC: Level 2 children love to choose their own music. Using the Music Survey Sheet (Section 7) record the songs your children have selected. Since we alternate activities with each song, it is not necessary to have non-stop, professional mixed music. The breaks between songs are actually a refreshing cue to change activities. A sample song list and choreography for this level can be found in this Section.

*S*tep music should be between 118-122 beats per minute. The suggested songs listed fall within the specific step guidelines. If you should choose to use different musical selections, count the beats per minute of the song desired for 10 seconds (beginning with the number 1), and multiply that number by 6. This will give you an estimation of how many beats per minute are in your desired selection. For example, if there were 20 beats counted in 10 seconds, the beats per minute of this selection would be 120 (20 x 6).

*S*IGNIFICANCE OF STEPPING WITH KIDS: This Group Choreography was the exact choreography used in the City KidZ Step research project with 11 & 12 year olds. See Section 9 on Research for the abstract and exact physiological and musculoskeletal findings of this program.

WARM UP
(5 Minutes)

Music: "Adam's Groove" by MC Hammer
(Theme song from Adam's Family Movie)

Make two circles of children (one inside the other)
The inner circle moves to the left
The outer circle moves to the right

As they are moving, they are shrugging their shoulders, waving their arms, rolling their shoulders, taking large steps, etc.

When the chorus is sung, the children stop and face a child in the other circle (inner circle faces outer circle). Together with their partner, they complete the following actions:

- Slap own thighs twice (with both hands)
- Clap own hands twice
- Shake partners right hand twice
- Shake partners left hand twice
- Slap own thighs twice
- Clap own hands twice
- Snap fingers four times

Repeat from the beginning, halting the circles on each chorus until the song ends

Movement Song 1 - "Too Legit to Quit" by MC Hammer

Basic Step Right Leg Lead - (32 counts of music)
Victory Step Right Leg Lead
Karate Kick
Hip Hop Jump on the floor to change lead legs

Repeat above with Left leg leading

Keep alternating between right and left lead legs until the end of the song.

NOTE: Once the leg movements have become familiar, add MC Hammer hand moves to the chorus: Two (hold up to fingers) Legit (Make letter L with hand), Two (hold up two fingers again), Quit (flat hand moving under chin)

Strength/Endurance Song 2 - "Black or White" by Michael Jackson

BiCep BeeBop (see Exercise How To's - Chapter 3)
Da Deltoids

Alternate these two exercises until the song ends
Allow for rest time when fatigue sets in

✓ Check Points - Keep Wrists Straight . . . Don't Pull With Your Body . . .

Movement Song 3 - "Achy Breaky Heart" by Billy Ray Cyrus

Begin atop the step

Cowboy Straddle Right Leg (32 counts)
Cowboy Straddle Knee
Look Out (get ready to change lead legs)
Cowboy Straddle Left Leg
Cowboy Straddle Knee
Look Out
Lunge Away
Look Out

NOTE: Once foot movements become familiar, add fun "cowboy" arms such as "lasso twirls", "knee slaps", "thumbs in the pocket"

Strength/Endurance Song 4 - "Ghostbusters" from Ghostbusters Movie Soundtrack

TraZapius (see Chapter 3 - Exercise How To's)
Tricep Truffle Punch
Alternate these two exercises until the end of the song
Allow for rest/recovery time during song, if needed

✓ Check Points - Keep Wrists Straight . . . Avoid Locking Elbow . . . Relax Shoulders

Movement Song 5 - "Good Vibrations" by Marky Mark OR JUMP by Kriss Kross

Basketball Shoot Right Leg Lead
Alternating Basketball Shoot
Basketball Shoot
Football V
Hip Hop on floor (to change legs)
Alternating Volleyball Set
Batter Up

Repeat from beginning with other lead leg

NOTE: Arm moves mimic sport in choreography

Strength/Endurance Song 6 - "Turtle Power"
by Partners in Kryme

Pec"Tur"talis
Quad Ra Bunga

> ✓ Check Points - Keep Wrists Straight . . . Knees Over Ankle Region . . . Hips No Lower
> Than Knee Level

Movement Song 7 - "Walk the Dinosaur" by Was Not Was

Basic Step Right Leg Lead
Hip Hop Jump (to switch legs)
Basic Step Left Leg Lead

Repeat above sequence until the chorus

Chorus: Walk to another child's step, slapping Hi-Fives
as pass other children

Repeat until song ends

NOTE: Roll arms, clap hands, slap thighs, walk the dinosaur head, hand motions to fit words in song

Strength/Endurance Song 8 - "The Right Stuff"
by New Kids On The Block

Kid Crunch (see Chapter 3 - Exercise How To's)
Kid Punch - Modified push ups plus "Air Boxing" for rests between sets

> ✓ Check Points : Beware Of Pulling On Head During Kid Crunch . . . Avoid Locking Elbows
> During Kid Punch

Cool Out Song 9 - "Freak Me" by Silk

OPTIONAL SONGS:
"That's What Friends Are For" by Dionne & Friends
"Heal The World" by Michael Jackson
"I Will Always Love You" by Whitney Houston

Statically stretch the following muscles for at least 20 seconds
Relax, breathe, cool off
> Hamstrings
> Quadriceps
> Biceps
> Trapezius
> Spine
> Triceps
> Abdominals
> Gastrocnemius

If time permits, use visualizations for children to further cool off:
> Melting ice cream
> Wilting flowers
> Tree blowing in wind
> Blossoming flower

*NOTE: Dino-Muscles™ has "dinosaur" stretch sequences that young children enjoy
following. See "Resources " in Section 10 Chapter on how to purchase Dino-Muscles™ .

"KidZ Step makes me feel
G-R-R-EAT!"

Sandara Medina, age 11

Creative Ideas

THE
MOVEMENT ZOO

Donate one wall of your facility or classroom for the Movement Zoo. As children learn each song, they can add the animals to the Movement Zoo wall. Get creative and paint a zoo background on large white butcher paper. Paint water pools, grasslands, cages, etc. so the animals can be placed on it later, as you progress through the program.

You may want to post the class' favorite "animal fact" near the pictures of the animals in the movement zoo.

All of the interesting information and facts for the animals can be found in the book entitled, ZOO CLUES, by Sheldon L. Gerstenfeld.

MOVEMENT CENTER

Objective

The children will engage in cooperative movement activities at the movement center.

Goals

Each child will come to the movement center at least once a day. The movement center is a place where children can:
- vent their energy
- explore movements
- exercise
- chart progresses
- learn about time/space/body

Needed

A designated area
Props (painted doll rods, plastic colorful plates, balls, steps,
        jump ropes, bean bags, mats, etc)

Set Up

Charting

Concepts Addressed
- Reading
- Graphing/Charting
- Motivation
- Self-Discipline
- Responsibility
- Cooperativeness

Design

Post a chart on the wall in the movement center. List all the names of the children. Across the top, write the dates or days of the week. Each child awards himself/herself a sticker for moving in the center. Goal is to get one sticker per day. If you go to the movement center more than once/day, no additional stickers are awarded.

Decide on your specific class goals (ex. Reward monthly, weekly, or bi-weekly successes).

Write your reward system on a posterboard so it is visible in the center. (ex. In one week's time, our class, which has 20 students, must have a total of 90 stickers in order to earn 30 minutes of "free-time").

Movement Activity

Concepts Addressed
- Balance
- Kinesthetic Awareness
- Concentration
- Math Skills
- Gross/Fine Motor Skills
- Coordination

Activities

Signs telling children what to do (with words and pictures) should be posted for children to read.

> *Examples:*
>
> Balance - Stand on one leg with a bean bag in each hand with one eye closed for 15 seconds. Now switch legs. (Use stop watch or timer)
>
> Step - Step up and down for 1 minute. Switch legs and repeat (Use timer/stop watch)
>
> Balls - Throw the ball in the air and catch it ten times without stopping
>
> Doll Rods - Roll the doll rods in your fingers of both hands. Then reach them up toward the ceiling ten times. Pass it under your legs ten times, then roll the rods in the opposite direction.

Message Board

Concepts Addressed
- Communication
- Cooperation
- Reading/Writing Skills

Activities

Leave a message to a friend encouraging him/her to keep moving in the movement center or just to say hi.

MIND/MOVEMENT JOURNALS (M&M's)

Objective

The children will keep a daily movement journal which will serve as a reminder of their committment to healthy movements.

Activity/Topic Ideas

Have children look through magazines and cut out pictures of people "moving" (i.e. walking, riding bikes, swimming, etc). Paste these in their journals. Write a sentence or story about the picture.

Decorate their movement journals with words and/or pictures of movements

Each day have children complete a M&M page (Mind/Movement). They can draw pictures, write words, use inventive spellings, or write stories about movements that help their bodies and minds become strong and healthy.

CULMINATING ACTIVITIES

Take a trip to the zoo
• List all the animals the children saw at the zoo that were in their program
• List or discuss the active movements the animals at the zoo were doing
• List or discuss the non-active movements the animals at the zoo were doing
• Draw pictures and/or write stories about the children's favorite animals at the zoo

Visit a Pet Store
• List or discuss all the animals that were seen at the pet store
• Categorize the animals seen at the pet store
• Count the number of different types of animals seen
    (i.e. how many different types of dogs, cats, birds, etc.)

Zoo to You Programs
Call your local zoo or pet store and schedule the animals to come to you

Animal Lovers Career Day
Invite a veterinarian/zoo keeper/etc. to discuss their careers with the children.

CirKID Step
A Youth Step
Circuit Program

The following program is the KidZ Step Circuit Program. The CirKid Step class can be set up as a group format where all children are executing the same circuit moves/exercises together, or as a Breakout program where all the children move around the room visiting individual stations with their partners and/or peers. See the following diagrams:

* = Step Placement

Group CirKid Class Set Up

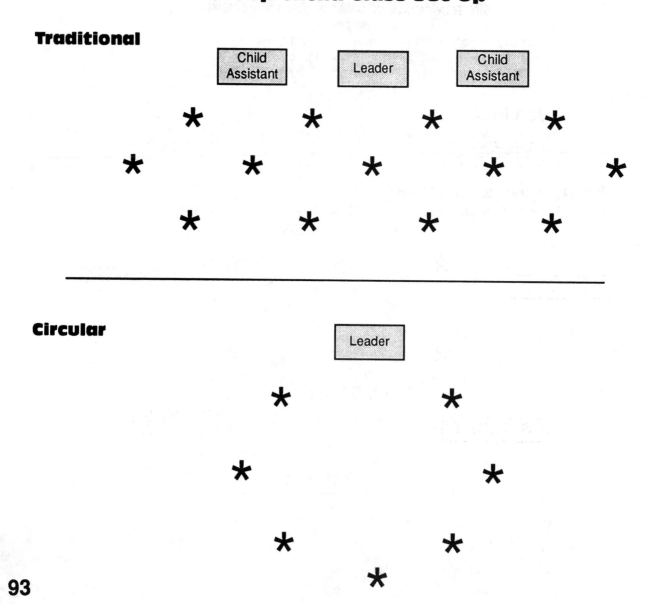

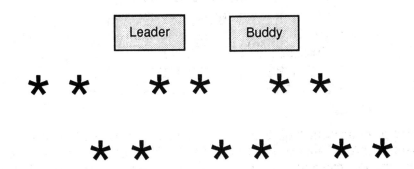

Breakout CirKid Class Format

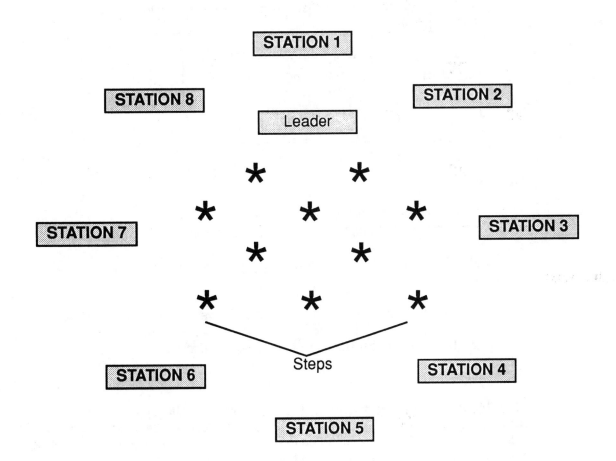

*T*he Circuit Kids Class can be used with both Levels 1 and 2. The only alteration may need to be the "titles" of the activities for Level 2 children (Whoa Horsey (Level 1) vs. Shoulder Raises (Level 2)).

*T*he class alternates two minutes of group step with two minutes of station activities (in both the Breakout and Group formats). The following will define and explain each activity. Refer to the Section on Terminology and Exercise How To's for specific execution directions.

<u>**STATION 1**</u> | **KID CRUNCH/KID PUNCH** | **ABDOMINALS/PECTORALS**

Kid Crunch

Equipment: 1 Step/2 children
1 mat/child

Positioning: One child is supine on the mat along the front of the step, feet atop the step at the short end. The other child is supine along the other side of the step facing the opposite direction with his/her feet atop the step at the opposite end.

Action: With the hands comfortably behind the head, not pulling on the head/neck, both children curl up simultaneously (exhaling), and give a HIGH FIVE slap to their partner, who is on the other side of the step. Hold the position, then lower down to the starting position (inhaling).

> ✔ Check Points: Slow And Controlled
> Breathing
> No Pulling On Head/neck
> Do Not Use Momentum

Kid Punch

Equipment: 1 Step/2 children
1 mat/child

Positioning: Children kneel on their mats with their hands atop the step, facing each other.

Action: Simultaneously, children bend elbows, bringing chest to the top of the step (inhale). Return to starting position (exhale). After 8 repetitions, children kneel upright and simulate "boxing air punches".

Repeat

*The children are given the opportunity to alternate between the Kid Crunch and Kid Punch as they desire. This allows them to become responsible for their own progress. As a "pair", they decide when to switch activities. This peer decision-making and coaching fosters cooperative support, encouragement, and motivation.

STATION 2 | **CLAP N SLAP** | **QUADRICEPS/HAMSTRINGS**

Equipment: 1 Step/2 children

Positioning: The children stand on opposite sides of their step, facing each other. Each child starts with both feet flat on the floor.

Action: Beginning with their right leg, they execute a step up squat. (Right foot atop the step, bend right knee 90 degrees, left foot remains on the floor). As they execute the step up squat, they slap left hands twice. Step the right off the step and return to starting position, clap own hands twice. Walk to other side of the step. Repeat with the left leg. Continue alternating legs until time is up.

> ✓ Check Points: Do Not Llunge More Than 90 Degrees
>   Abdominals Held in
>   Knee Is aligned Over Heel Area
>   Avoid Leaning Forward
>   Control

STATION 3 | **PASS N SQUAT** | **QUADRICEPS/ABDUCTORS**

Equipment: 1 Step/2 children
                 Balls or Stuffed Animals

Positioning: Children face each other on opposite sides of the step with the right sides of their bodies to the side of the step.

Action: Children take one side squat onto the step with the foot that is closest to the step. At the same time, they "fake" pass the prop to their partner twice. The third time, they move across the top of the step, ending up on the other side of the step. As they are passing across the top, they pass the prop to their partner. Repeat from above with the partner now in possession of the prop.

STATION 4 | **RIDE EM' COWBOY** | **DELTOIDS/TRAPEZIUS**

Equipment: 1 Step/2 children
                 SPRI QuikFit

Positioning: Seated side by side atop the step. One end of the QuikFit is beneath the arch of the child's foot. (Make sure the foot stays in contact with the floor to avoid the QuikFit from snapping up.) Both hands hold the other end of the QuikFit.

Action: Hands begin on the lap. Move hands up and bring under the chin, contracting the deltoids (exhale). Hold and return to the starting position.
         *Option - when returning to starting position, move the body up and
           down as if riding a horse.

> ✓ Check Points: Abdominals Held Tightly
>   Keep Shoulders Down And Relaxed
>   Control

WHOA HORSEY

Equipment: 1 Step/2 children
SPRI QuikFit

Positioning: Seated side by side atop the step. One end of the QuikFit is beneath the arch of the children's foot. (Make sure the foot stays in contact with the floor to avoid the QuikFit from snapping up.) Both hands hold the other end of the QuikFit.

Action: The QuikFit is in the right hand and is resting on the lap. The left hand is holding onto the other end of the QuikFit. Without turning the body, pull the QuikFit up toward the right shoulder. The elbow comes slightly behind the body. (This simulates pulling the reins on a horse (exhale). Hold and then return to the starting position. Repeat for one set and switch to the opposite hand.

> ✓ Check Points: Abdominals Held Tightly
> Keep Shoulders Down And Relaxed
> Avoid Twisting Torso To Move The Arm
> Keep The Wrist Straight As Executing Exercise

**Children alternate between these two exercises as they desire.

ROW BOAT

Equipment: 1 Step per child
Children facing each other
2 QuikFits per child

Positioning: Children sit facing each other with feet flat on the floor. Each child has a QuikFit. The child holds one end of one QuikFit in his/her right hand. The other QuikFit is held in the left hand of each child. The QuikFits will make the letter "X" as they cross each other.

Action: Begin with the shoulders down, hands rested on the lap. Without leaning or moving the torso, the children simultaneously pull the QuikFits so the scapula abducts. The elbows come behind the body. The children say "Row Row Row" during the hold (exhale). Return to starting position. Children say "The Boat" (inhale).

> ✓ Check points: Shoulders Relaxed
> Abdominals Held Tightly
> Do Not Lean Or Move Torso
> Both Children Must Pull At The Same Time
> With The Same Force

HITCH HIKE

Equipment: 1 Step per child
Children facing each other
1 QuikFits per child

Positioning: Children sit facing each other with feet flat on the floor.
Each child has a QuikFit. The child holds one end of one QuikFit in his/her
right hand. The other QuikFit is held in the left hand of each child. The
QuikFit will make the letter "X" as they cross each other.

Action: Begin in the same position as previously. This time, only one arm
will move at a time. Start with their right arms, bent at the elbow; bring
the palm of the hand toward the right shoulder with the thumb turned out, as if
hitch hiking (exhale). Hold and then return to starting position (inhale).
Repeat for one set, then switch to opposite arm.

*Children can alternate between Row Boats and Hitch Hikes as they desire.

QUAD RA BUNGA

Equipment: Same as above

Positioning: Standing on opposite sides of the step, right sides next
to step.

Action: Beginning with right legs, children squat (knee 90 degree angle)
sideways so right leg comes atop the step. Children hold the squat and
then return to starting position. Children take hops, moving around the
step and repeat from beginning. When they get back to their original
position, they repeat with left leg.

✓ Check points:	Abdominals Held In
	Control
	Knee Only Flexes To 90 Degree Angle

*Note: Children yell "Quad Ra Bunga" when doing squat

98

STATION 6 | **MONSTER SCARE** | **PECTORALS/DELTOIDS/
QUADRICEPS**

Equipment: 1 Step per child
                1 QuikFit per child

Positioning: Children sit atop the step with their backs to each other. One child holds one end of the QuikFit in his/her right hand while the other end of the QuikFit passes under his/her arm. The other QuikFit is held in the left hand of the child while the other end of the QuikFit is in his/her partners right hand. The QuikFits run parallel to each other. The children begin the exercise with their hands at shoulder level, QuikFits passing under their arms, elbows pointing downward.

Action: The action is a See Saw motion. One child reaches forward on the count of one (exhale). The child lets out a "monster scream". On the count of two, the child returns to starting position (inhale). Both children stand up on the count of three and return to the starting position on the count of four. The entire sequence repeats itself with the opposite child reaching forward.

✓ Check points: Keep Shoulders Down And Relaxed
                       Hold Abdominals In
                       Control
                       Do Not Lock Elbows

STATION 7 | **OBSTACLES** |

| **(This station can only be used with the Breakout format)** |

Equipment: The following equipment gets set up in an obstacle set up, as you desire:

- 4-5 steps randomly set
- hula hoops
- jump ropes
- balls
- cones
- slide boards
- books (for balancing on head)

Action: Children move through the obstacle course reading the signs and executing the moves until their time is up. Sample:

- Straddle walk the steps
- 4 hula hoop twists
- 8 consecutive slides on the slide boards
- Play catch with a partner, 2 x 3 times
- Jump rope (10 - 2) times
- Balance a book on your head and walk from cone
      to cone and back to starting place

NOTE: Write out the obstacle activities on poster boards and affix them near each prop at the obstacle station. As children move through the obstacle course, they will enjoy reading the signs and completing the movements.

I WANT TO BE . . .

I Want To Be . . . (This station can only be used with the Breakout Format)

Equipment: 1 step/child
Baseball cap, Nerf Baseball Bat, Nerf Football,
Construction Worker's Hat, Karate Short Rope,
TuTu (ballerina), Jewelery & Plum Feathers (dancer)

Action: Children dress up with their choice of props and act out the actions of their selected professionals. The only requirement is that they creatively and safely execute the movements on and around the steps.

KidRap
Scope and Sequence

Goal: To feel comfortable and valued as a member of the KidZ Step Class

MAIN OBJECTIVES	LEVEL 1	LEVEL 2
Name interests of a classmate	•	•
Introduces a friend to the class	•	•
Names different ways of giving	•	•
Demonstrates helpful behaviors	•	•
Contributes his/her ideas to the group	•	•

Goal: Use interpersonal skills to relate to their peers

MAIN OBJECTIVES	LEVEL 1	LEVEL 2
Participates in cooperative activities	•	•
Demonstrates listening to other's messages	•	•
Demonstrates sharing behaviors	•	•
Demonstrates responding in a positive way to negative behaviors	•	•
Demonstrates how to resolve a conflict by reaching a positive agreement		•

Goal: Learning how to make positive, responsible decisions and saying "No" to harmful ones

MAIN OBJECTIVES	LEVEL 1	LEVEL 2
Predicts positive and negative consequences of a decision	•	•
Classifies decisions as positive or negative	•	•
Name some decisions he/she makes every day	•	•
Explain difference between positive and negative peer pressure	•	•
Name negative peer pressure students may face	•	•
Say "Yes" to helpful decisions and "No" to harmful ones	•	•

Goal: To incorporate healthy fitness choices into their lifestyles

MAIN OBJECTIVES	LEVEL 1	LEVEL 2
Explain how the heart works and its importance to life	•	•
Identify a healthy well-balanced diet	•	•
Name some healthy snacks	•	•
Identify activities that will strengthen the heart	•	•
Identify the Dino-Muscles™ and how they're used daily	•	•
Discuss the difference between "overfat" and "overweight"		•
Discuss problems with dieting		•
Discuss "positive body image"		•
Discuss the media's portrayal of the "perfect body"		•

KidRap

The following KidRaps will take approximately 5 minutes and should be used to close each KidZ Step class following the cool out period. There are 12 KidRap topics that are correlated to the objectives listed in the scope and sequence. Always begin the KidRap session by explaining the purpose of the day's rap. Additionally, the Dino-Muscles™ curriculum supplementation can be integrated daily to educate the children about the anatomical and kinesiological theories related to their everyday movements. The KidRap topics can be selected at random depending on your needs or preferences. For easier organization of your KidRap discussions, use the "log bar" provided in the margin to serve as a reminder of the dates you selected each topic.

Rap 1
Level Appropriateness: All

Purpose: Life is full of decisions. WE need to be aware of making safe, smart choices when given the opportunity to do so. It's OK to say "Yes", as long as the consequences of this decision will be positive and safe. However, if an adult or other child asks you to do something harmful, you need to have the strength to say "No". Let's talk about some "real-life" situations that some children have encountered and see if we can think about what we would do in these same situations, and what our consequences would be.

Strategy: Let's think of ways to say "Yes". Allow children time to "rap". Some of their discussions should include the words Okay, Alright, Sure, I'm Game, Uh-Huh, etc. Now let's think of ways to say "No. Allow children time to "rap". Some of their discussions should include the words, "No thanks, No way, I can't, I won't, I don't want to, My mom won't let me".

Activity: Now let's rap about the following situations. Tell which situations are harmful and explain why and what consequences would arise.

Topics: Level 1

    A - Your big brother asks you to go rollerskating

    B - Your aunt asks you to come over for dinner

    C - An adult, you don't know very well, invites you to go to a carnival and says you don't need to ask your parents

    D - A friend invites you to his/her birthday party

    E - A friend invites you to come over when his/her parents aren't home

    F - Your brother tells you to take some money from your mom's purse and he'll go buy you some candy

    G - Some kids tell you to pull the fire alarm at school for $10

    H - Your dad gives you some aspirin for your cold

    I - A friend wants you to call someone a "sissy"

Log Bar

Rap 2

Purpose: Using the same purpose as in Rap 1, we will expand and discuss the three step decision making process:
Think about your choices and consequences
Choose the one that is helpful or positive
Do it!!!

Strategy: Let's talk about peer pressure.

Activity: All levels
• What is peer pressure?
• Can it be beneficial? How?
• Can it be harmful? How? When?
• What can we do when we are getting pressured by our peers to do harmful things?

Rap 3

Log Bar

Purpose: We all get angry sometimes. Let's rap about positive ways to respond to anger.

Strategy: Have the children rap about what they say and do when they're angry. What makes them really angry?

Activity: All Levels
• What gets you angry?
• How do you feel after you get angry?
• How do you think the other person feels?
• What do you usually do after that?

* Talk about some ways to handle angry feelings.
• Count to 10 and calm down, take a few deep breaths
• Talk About It! We need to say exactly what is making us mad. For example, "I don't like it when you call me _____". OR Stop pinching me, it really hurts, and I don't like it.
• Cool Off Alone.
Sometimes when we get upset, we need time alone away from people.

104

Rap 4

Purpose: To develop good listening habits

Strategy: Let's rap about what are some ways to let people know you're listening to them. (Ex. Look at them, nod your head, agree with them, say "Yes or Uh-Huh or Really") and ways to be unattentive (Ex. Read the paper, don't look at them, no response at all)

Activity: All levels
• Rap about ways to be an inattentive listener
• How do you feel when someone doesn't listen to you?
• What do you do to try to get them to listen?
• How can you be a better listener?
• Let's rap about the time someone didn't listen to you. How did you feel? What could you have said to get their attention?

Rap 5

Log Bar

Purpose: To find positive ways to resolve conflicts

Strategy: Rap about positive things we can do to resolve problems and conflicts.

Activity: Level 1

A   *Anna wanted to use Maria's brand new crayons, but Maria didn't want to let Anna use them because Anna had her own crayons. Maria's crayons were brand new, and Anna's were old. Anna said, "I hate you Maria. I'm not your friend anymore." Maria started crying.
What could Maria do to solve this conflict?

B   *Brian, Billy, and Marcos were playing at the park. Brian and Billy were playing catch. Marcos was waiting his turn. Brian missed the ball. The ball went through Mrs. Jones kitchen window. The boys ran away. Later, Mrs. Jones went to each of the boys houses. Brian and Billy were brothers. They both said Marcos did it. (Brian lied for his brother so Billy wouldn't get into trouble). Mrs. Jones went to Marco's house to accuse Marcos of breaking her window. Marcos said that Billy did it. He told her how he missed the ball, but Billy threw it. Mrs. Jones didn't believe him because both Billy and Brian said he did it. What should Marcos do?

How does he feel being accused of something he really didn't do? Have you ever been accused of something you really didn't do? Let's rap about it.

105

Rap 5
(Continued)

Activity: Level 2

A   Nicole and Beth both like Michael. Michael decides that he likes Nicole because she is prettier than Beth. Beth is really angry at Nicole and threatens to never be her friend again if she likes Michael. Beth starts telling false rumors about Nicole and Michael in hopes that Michael will like her, not Nicole. If you were Nicole, how would you feel? What could you do?
Have you ever felt like Nicole?   Let's rap about it.

B   Tim and Vernon met up with Jose and Danny. They all decided to go play catch at the park. After an hour, they became thirsty. They walked to the corner store for some pop. Danny didn't have any money and Tim, Vernon, and Jose only had enough money for their soft drinks. Jose suggests that Danny just take a pop while the rest of them are at the counter buying theirs. The store owner won't miss a little can of pop. Besides, Danny was really thirsty and had no money.
What decision should Danny make?
What are the consequences he has to face?
Have you ever been in a situation like Danny?
Let's rap about it.

Rap 6

Purpose: To find some interests of a classmate and introduce that classmate to the group.

Strategy: Allowing children to mingle and socialize with their peers.

Activity: All levels
Make one set of number pairs (Ex. 1,1,2,2,3,3,4,4, etc) so each child will have a number. Mix up the numbers so the children can't see the numbers they select. Each child draws a number. At the signal, the children search the room looking for the child who has the same number as them. Once this child has been found, he/she who has the same number as them. Once this child has been found, he/she must "rap" with the child and find out the child's favorite food, favorite color, and favorite activity (i.e. running, baseball, playing dolls, etc).

Then have each pair of children introduce their partner to the group telling something they learned about their partner.

106

Rap 7

Purpose: To identify a variety of ways to "give".

Strategy: Let's rap about ways we can "give" to make someone happy. (Ex. hugs, pats on back, words of encouragement or praise, do something nice, help someone, a gift, letter, phone call, etc) What's the difference between "Material" gifts and "Non-Material" gifts?

Activity: All levels
*John and Laura's parents are divorced. They live with their mom, but she works everyday and doesn't get home til 6:30 p.m. John and Laurie come home from school everyday and do their homework and watch TV. They can't wait until their mom gets home because she always brings them a "treat or gift". They don't really like it when their dad takes care of them. He doesn't buy them things like their mom does. He only plays with them and takes them everywhere he goes. He likes going to libraries, museums, etc.
    Let's rap about what John and Laura are feeling.

Rap 8

Purpose: To identify specific components of a healthy well-balanced diet.

Strategy: Discuss the new "Food Pyramid" and its relation to living a healthy lifestyle. Discuss the importance of moderation. Discuss ways of making "healthy" food "unhealthy" (i.e., frying, buttering, etc). Contact the Center for Science in the Public Interest, Suite 300, 1875 Connecticut Avenue NW, Washington D.C., 20009, for a copy of the "Food Pyramid".

Activity: All levels
A   • Let's rap about what you eat at home.
        • What are healthy snacks?
        • Let's rap about eating out.
        • What are healthy choices at a restaurant?
        • What are unhealthy choices?
        • Talk about overdoing a good thing and the importance of fat and
            calories for children.

B   *Julia doesn't want to be fat when she gets older. She has vowed to
never eat any fat again. At her sister's birthday party, she wouldn't even take
a small piece of birthday cake. At Halloween, she gave all her candy to her
sister. And on Easter, she threw her treats in the garbage. When her mom makes
fried foods for dinner, Julia eats it and then leaves the table quickly to go to the
bathroom.

        What do you think Julia is doing? What could you tell her?

107

Rap 9

Purpose: To identify activities that keep your heart and muscles strong and healthy.

Strategy: Discuss the difference between movements and activities that strengthen your heart versus those that strengthen your muscles. Discuss the importance of both.

Activity: Let's rap about all the things you do each day that could be categorized as a "heart strengthening" activity. Now let's rap about how your muscles helped you do things today. What do you need strong hearts and muscles for?

Rap 10

Purpose: Using the Dino-Muscles™ lessons spend a few weeks teaching the children the importance of their muscles, where their muscles are, what their muscles do for them daily, etc.

Strategy: Use the Dino-Muscles™ characters to teach the children about muscles.

Activity: Let the children rap about things their specific muscles help them do daily. Example:
        Biceps - carry books to school
        Deltoids - raise arms overhead
        Quadriceps - climb stairs

Rap 11

Purpose: To identify life threatening diseases related to unhealthy lifestyles.

Strategy: Discuss healthy versus unhealthy lifestyles.

Healthy	Unhealthy
lean	overfat
active	inactive
alert	lazy
good eating	poor eating
positive self image	negative self image
strong	weak/sickly
non-smoker	smoker
no drug use	drug use
no or little alcohol consumption	excessive alcohol consumption
minimal medications taken	excessive medications taken
safe sex (Level 2 only option)	unsafe sex (Level 2 only option)

Activity: All Levels
• Let's rap about diseases that have been linked to unhealthy lifestyles. Tell what you know about prevention, as well as the disease itself. (Ex. Cancer, Heart Disease, Stroke, Aids, Diabetes)

Rap 12 (Level 2)

Purpose: To develop positive "body images" through realistic self acceptance.

Strategy: To rap about individual realistic body images, the influence of media on today's society, the influence of our genes in determining our body types, and the feelings we have about our "bodies".

Activity: (Boys and Girls Should be Rapped With Separately)
A Let's rap about how we feel about our bodies. What physical changes have you noticed in the past years? What feelings have you experienced about these changes? What do you think about growing up?

B Let's rap about what our parents/grandparents bodies are like now as well as when they were younger. Rap about any correlations.

C Let's rap about what we see on TV and in the magazines as the ideal "body". How do they feel about that image?

Rap 12
Continued

D   Sara hates herself. She is 5 feet tall and weighs 100 pounds. She doesn't like her hair, her mole on her face, or her height. She wants to look like the girl on the cover of "TEEN" Magazine; 5'5, thin, blonde hair, clear skin, big lips and eyes, and a great body. Sara has decided to go on a "no eating" diet and exercise every day. When she turns 16, she's 14 now, she's going to dye her hair blonde. Her mom is concerned about Sara's new interest in watching what she eats. Sara's mom started to force Sara to eat. After dinner, Sara quickly goes to the bathroom and vomits up her dinner. She feels real tired all the time, but she is losing weight. She's down to 80 pounds now and is trying to lose just a few more pounds.

Let's rap about Sara: What is happening to her?
Is what she's doing all right?
What would you suggest to her?
What if Sara doesn't stop what he's doing?

Log Bar

Boys Scenario:
E   Joey is 5' tall and is really thin. All the boys tease him because of his size. He'd give anything to grow and get some muscles. He started reading some books and has decided to start lifting weights and eating like the "muscle men". He's eating alot of eggs and had his mom buy some special drink to gain weight. He also started to do a lot of exercises at home to help him get muscles. His cousin, who is a body builder gave him some pills to take to make his muscles grow. After a few months Joey has finally started to gain some weight and grow some muscles. He feels a little shaky when he forgets to take his muscle pills and has been really tired lately.

Let's rap about Joey: What is going on here?
What could some positive consequences be?
What could some negative consequences be?
What would you suggest to Joey?

110

PROP SHOP

The following are activities using a fun-filled approach to using the step as a prop in a game-like environment.

JINGLE JANGLE JAM TAG

Ages: 5-8

Equipment: Markers for boundaries
                 Bases/Hula-Hoops for "Safe-T-Zone"
                 Holiday Bells (on a necklace string or wrist bracelet)

Set Up: Choose two or three "Janglers", depending on the size of the group (one "Jangler" for every six to eight runners). Each "Jangler" gets some Holiday Bells.

Description: Jingle Jangle Jam Tag is a very active game that is a great "ice breaker" to start a class. The game is played much like Freeze Tag. Steps are placed outside the boundary markers. This comprises the "Safe-T-Zone". If in the "Safe-T-Zone", the children step up and down on the step, hop over the bases, or rest in the hula-hoops. Runners who are tagged in the playing field become frozen; that is, they remain where they were tagged without moving. Frozen runners can be freed if they are tagged by another runner.

In Jingle Jangle Jam Tag, a runner in the playing field may avoid being tagged by quickly sitting down and singing one line of a "Holiday Song" (i.e. *Jingle Bells, Jingle Bells, Jingle All the Way*). This protects the runner for five seconds (or until the "Jangler" has gone away). A runner who is tagged before sitting down and singing the tune is frozen.

Set a time limit for each round of the game and rotate "Janglers", so all children get a turn.

Note: If children are younger or not familiar with "Holiday Tunes", sing a few together as a group to give them ideas. Suggested tunes include "Jingle Bells", "Rudolph the Red-Nosed Reindeer", "Santa Clause Is Coming To Town", "Silent Night", and "Twelve Days of Christmas".

FOUR CORNERS STEP

Level: Ages 9-12

Equipment: Steps
Hula-Hoops
Ribbons
Plastic Water Jugs filled halfway with sand

Set Up: Using the four corners of the room, set up the following stations:

First Corner: Basic Step 8 on each leg
Football V 8 on each leg
Batter Up 8 on each leg

Second Corner: Hula Hoop 10 times
Karate Kick 8 on each leg
Kid Crunch 8 curls

Third Corner: Basic Step with Ribbons 8 on each leg
Volleyball 8 on each leg
Hop in place 8 times

Fourth Corner: Victory Step 8 on each leg
Bicep BeeBop with jugs 8 with each arm
Quad-Ra-Bungas 8 times

Description: The children perform the first movement on their sign at their corner the designated amount of time, then they move to the next corner. When they return to their starting corner, they do the second movement/exercise. This repeats until all children have gone through all three exercises/ movements at all four corners of the room. Play music throughout the activity to keep the class motivated.

WILD CARD PARTNER STEP

Level: Ages 8-12

Equipment: Steps
Task Cards in baggies
Colored Construction Paper
Jump Ropes
Bean Bags
Brown Paper Bag

Set-Up: Pair Steps around perimeter of the room. Place a piece of colored construction paper in front of the pair of steps to color code the station. Place baggie and task cards on the floor next to the construction paper. Cut one 1 x 2 piece of construction paper from each colored station and place in a brown paper bag. Have pairs sit in center of room.

Description: Each pair picks a piece a construction paper from the brown bag to designate where they are to go when the music starts playing. Start the music. The pairs of children run to the step that matches their color. They take one task card out of the baggie, read it, and begin following the task until the music stops. When the music stops, all pairs must run back to the center of the room and sit down. The game repeats itself so all children get to choose different stations each time.

Sample Tasks:
- Do 10 pushups with your hands on the steps, and your feet on the floor
- Do 4 Karate Kicks with each leg
- Hop around your step 4 times
- Leap over your step

ROLLING DICE STEP

Level: Ages 8-12

Equipment: Steps
Square cardboard boxes
Tape
Markers

Set-Up: Set up steps in pairs around the room. Tape edges of box to secure. Using colorful markers, write step names on each side of the boxes. On one box, write "slow", "medium" and "fast" on each side until all sides are filled up.

Description: Working in pairs, children roll their "step dice" to see which step they'll do when the music starts playing. The teacher rolls the "slow-medium-fast" dice in the center of the class. All steppers will execute their step move according to the speed designated on the center dice. Children stop and roll their dice again after the music stops (approximately every 45 seconds).

STEP LEADER GO & FREEZE!

Level: All

Equipment: Steps arranged in large circle
One step in the center of the circle
Music

Description: One student stands in the center of the circle and calls out a step move (see description of terms), and which foot to begin with.

The teacher puts the music on. The children begin when the Step Leader says GO!. When the music stops, the Leader says FREEZE! The Leader gets off his/her step, closes his/her eyes, spins around and picks a new Step Leader.
*This game can also be played using non-step movements (like marching, hopping, jumping, and running).

RIBBON FUN STEP

Level: All

Equipment: Steps arranged in a geometric shape of your choice
                  Music (child selected)
                  Ribbons or streamers of various colors

Description: Using ribbons/streamers, children step to music doing the following movements:

March atop step and make BIG circles with Ribbon in right hand. Change to other foot stepping up first, and left hand.

Repeat different step moves (see terminology section) and make ribbons move in the following ways:

Like a Snake	Up and Down
Above Your Head	Side To Side

Note: Remember to alternate arms and legs to balance the movements.

DINO-MUSCLES ®

A Learning Guide to Basic Muscle Anatomy

By
ANDREW PAUL BONSALL

The **Dino-Muscles**® chapter covers 10 major muscles of the body, including the heart. The first page of each lesson illustrates a fictional dinosaur performing his or her favorite skill in relation to the muscle of the lesson. The corresponding page includes a technical illustration and a storyline about the Dino-Muscle® character.

Each storyline follows a similar format:

Sentence 1: Introduces the Dino-Muscles® character

Sentence 2: Describes how the Dino-Muscles® character got its name

Sentence 3: Describes the favorite activity that Dino-Muscles® character performs

Sentence 4: Describes an activity for the students to palpate (feel) the muscle, along with a brief statement about the function of the muscle

Sentence 5: Asks questions of other activities that can be performed by that muscle

Sentence 6: Answers the question

TABLE OF CONTENTS

CARDIAC

CARDIAC
(the heart)
kär'de-ak

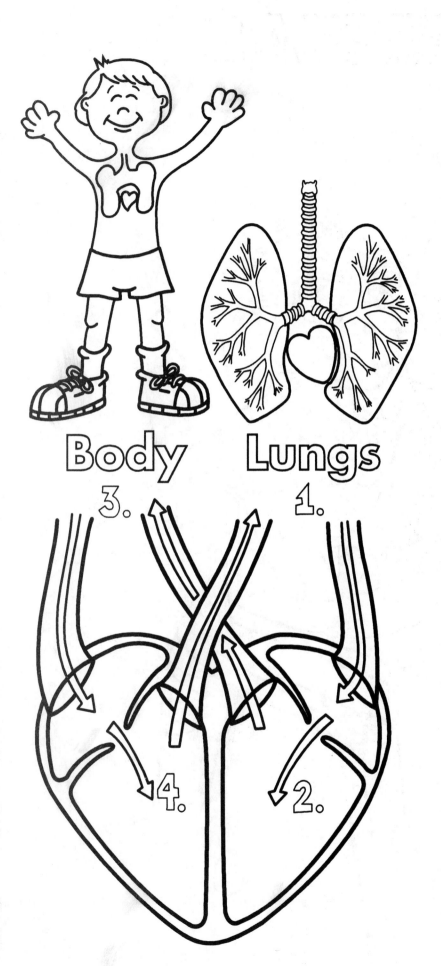

Body

Lungs

3.

1.

4.

2.

Cardiac the Dinosaur has a favorite muscle, the heart.

She is called Cardiac because "cardiac" means anything related to the heart.

The heart is her favorite muscle because she likes to dance a long time.

Taking Your Pulse
Put two fingers together, move your fingers below your jaw, and gently push in on your neck. Can you feel your pulse? That is the blood your heart pumps to your body so you have energy to play and think.

What activities does the heart help you do for a long time?

Swimming
Dancing
Bicycling
Skating
Walking
Aerobics

114

TRAPEZIUS

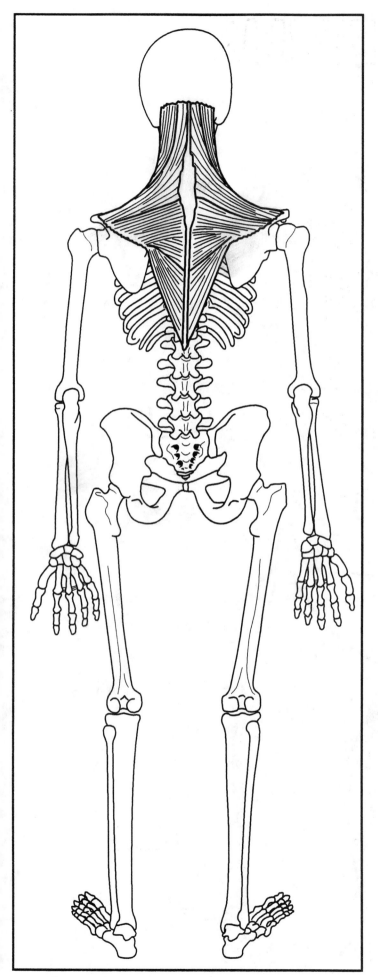

TRAPEZIUS
(the back of the neck & shoulders)
trah-pe'ze-us

Trapezius the Dinosaur has a favorite muscle, the trapezius muscle.

It is called the trapezius because it resembles the shape of the four-sided trapezoid:

The trapezius muscle is his favorite muscle because it helps him sit up straight in his seat, and that makes his teacher happy.

Find Your Trapezius
Squeeze the top of your shoulder. That is the top of your trapezius muscle. Lift that shoulder and you can feel it work. The trapezius muscle lifts and pulls back the shoulder.

What activities does the trapezius muscle help you do?
    Raising your head
    Swinging a tennis racket
    Shrugging your shoulders
    Hugging

BICEPS

117

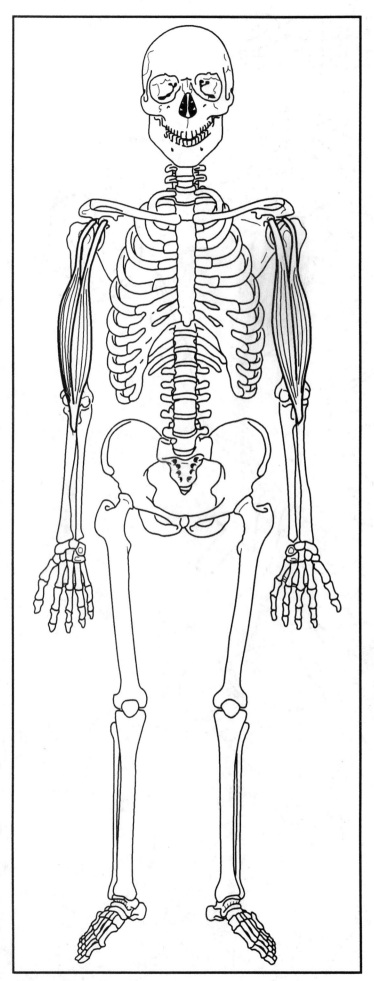

BICEPS
(the front of the arm)
bi'seps

Biceps the Dinosaur has a favorite muscle, the biceps muscle.

It is called the biceps because the **"bi"** part of its name means **"two"**, and the **"ceps"** part means **"heads"**. Therefore, biceps means **"two heads"**.

The biceps muscle is his favorite muscle because the biceps muscle helps him lift heavy things. Biceps the Dinosaur likes to lift dumbbells, so he can get stronger.

Find Your Biceps
Hold your arm out in front of you with your palm up. Squeeze the front of your upper arm with your other hand. That is your biceps muscle. Now, bring your hand towards your nose and you can feel it work. When the biceps muscle contracts, it flexes the forearm at the elbow joint.

What activities does the biceps muscle help you do?
Chin-ups
Tether ball
Hugging
Carrying books

118

TRICEPS

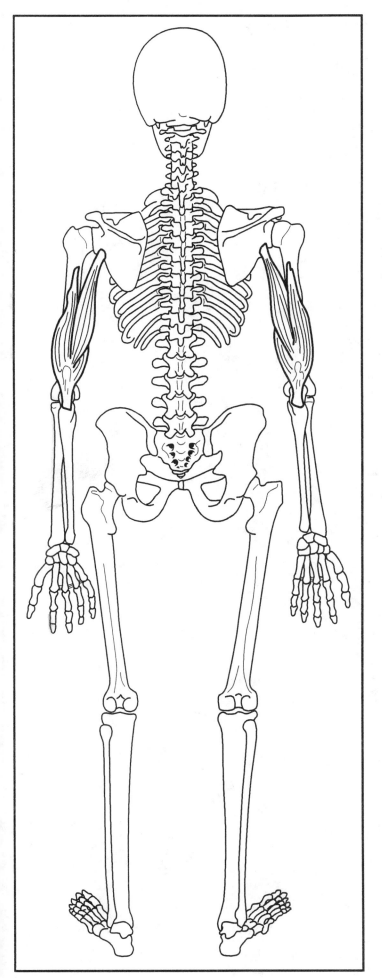

TRICEPS
(the back of the arm)
tri'seps

Triceps the Dinosaur has a favorite muscle, the triceps muscle.

It is called triceps because it has three heads. The **"tri"** part of its name means **"three"**, and the **"ceps"** part means **"heads"**. Therefore, triceps means **"three heads"**.

The triceps muscle is her favorite muscle because it helps her throw a ball far.

Find Your Triceps
Put your hand near your head and pretend you are going to throw a ball. Squeeze the back of your upper arm with your other hand. That is your triceps muscle. Now, pretend to throw the ball and extend your hand away from you. You can feel your triceps muscle working. When the triceps muscle contracts, it extends the forearm at the elbow joint.

What activities does the triceps muscle help your do?
>   Push-ups
>   Swinging a bat
>   Bouncing a ball
>   Handball

120

RECTUS ABDOMINIS

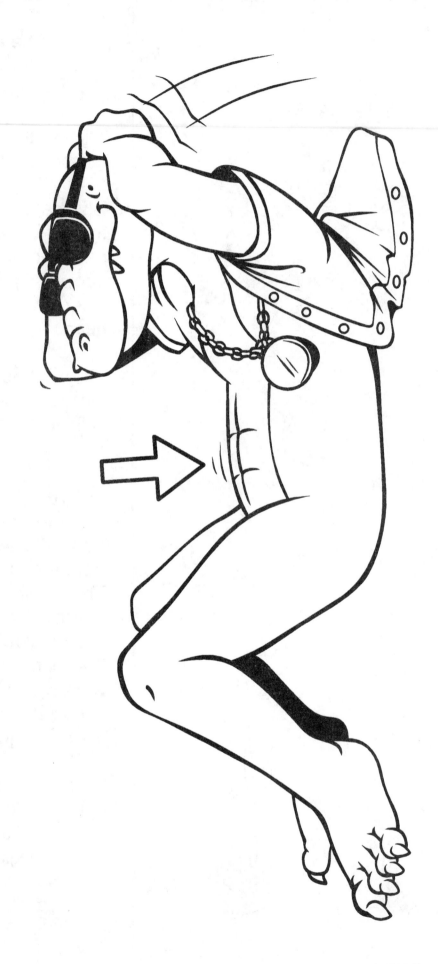

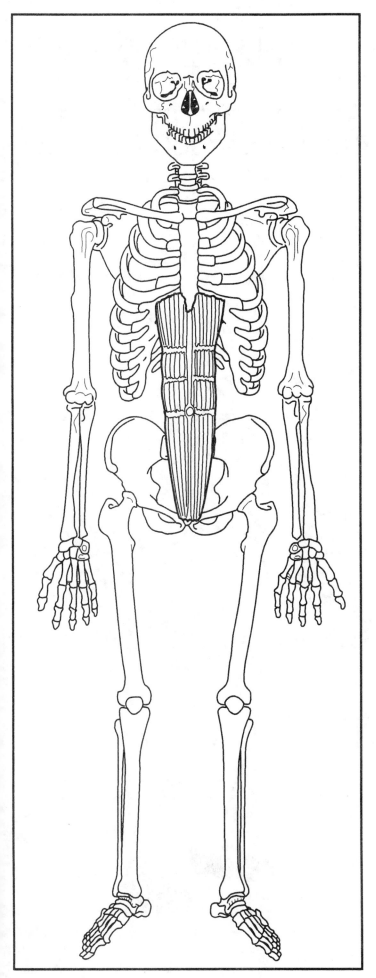

RECTUS ABDOMINIS
(abdomen)
rek'tus ab-dom'i-nis

Rectus Abdominis the Dinosaur has a favorite muscle, the rectus abdominis muscle.

It is called the rectus abdominis because **"rectus"** means **"straight"**, and **"abdominis"** means **"belly"** or **"abdomen"**. Therefore, rectus abdominis means **"straight muscle of the belly"**.

The rectus abdominis is his favorite muscle because it helps him do sit-ups.

Find Your Rectus Abdominis
Lay on your back, bend your knees, and put your hands on your abdomen (belly). Now, try to do a sit-up. You can feel your rectus abdominis working. The rectus abdominis pulls the chest towards the hips.

What activities does the rectus abdominis muscle help you do?
    Sit-ups
    Running
    Throwing
    Jumping
    Standing up straight

122

EXTERNAL & INTERNAL OBLIQUE ABDOMINALS

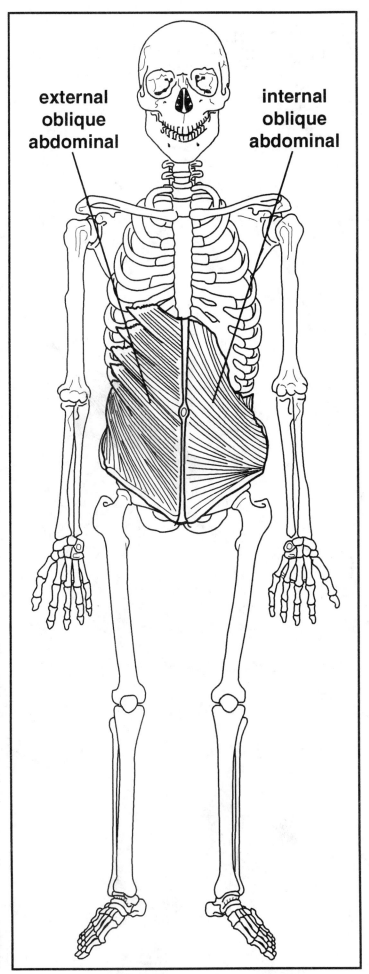

external oblique abdominal

internal oblique abdominal

EXTERNAL & INTERNAL OBLIQUE ABDOMINALS
(the sides of the abdomen)
o-bleek' ab-dom'i-nals

External and Internal Oblique Abdominal the Dinosaurs are twins. They have favorite muscles called the external and internal oblique abdominals.

They are called obliques because **"oblique"** means **"at an angle"**. **"External"** means **"towards the outside"**, and **"internal"** means **"towards the inside"**.

The oblique abdominal muscles are their favorite muscles because they help them dance and use a hula-hoop.

Find Your Oblique Abdominals
Put your hands on the sides of your abdomen (belly). That is where your external and internal oblique abdominals are. If you start twisting from side to side, you can feel them working. The oblique abdominals twist your shoulders towards the opposite hip.

What activities do the external and internal oblique abdominal muscles help you do?
Dancing
Hula-hooping
Throwing a ball
Swinging a bat
Sit-ups

124

QUADRICEPS

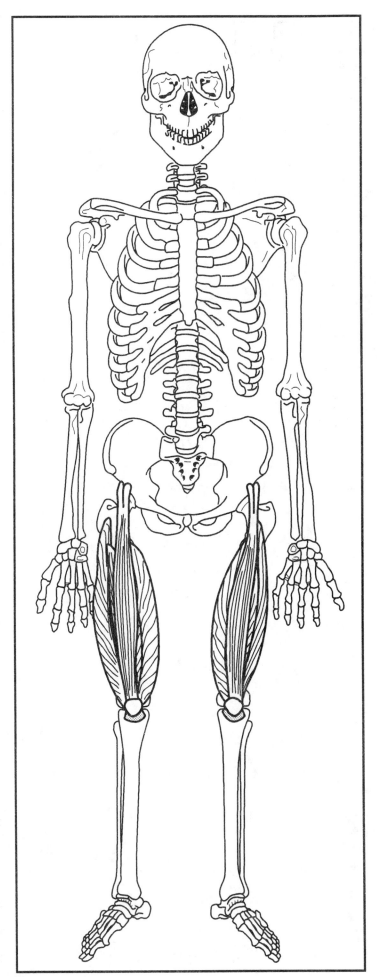

QUADRICEPS
(the front of the thigh)
kwöd'ri-seps

Quadriceps the Dinosaur has a favorite muscle, the quadriceps muscle.

It is called the quadriceps because the "**quad**" part of its name means "**four**", and the "**ceps**" part means "**heads**". Therefore, quadriceps means "**four heads**".

The quadriceps muscle is his favorite muscle because it helps him kick a soccer ball far.

Find Your Quadriceps
Stand up and lift one knee. Squeeze the front of your thigh just above your knee. That is your quadriceps muscle. Now, extend your leg out and you can feel it work. When the quadriceps muscle contracts, it extends the leg at the knee.

What activities does the quadriceps muscle help you do?
Kicking
Jumping
Running
Swimming
Standing up

126

GASTROCNEMIUS

GASTROCNEMIUS
(the back of the leg)
gas"trok-ne'me-us

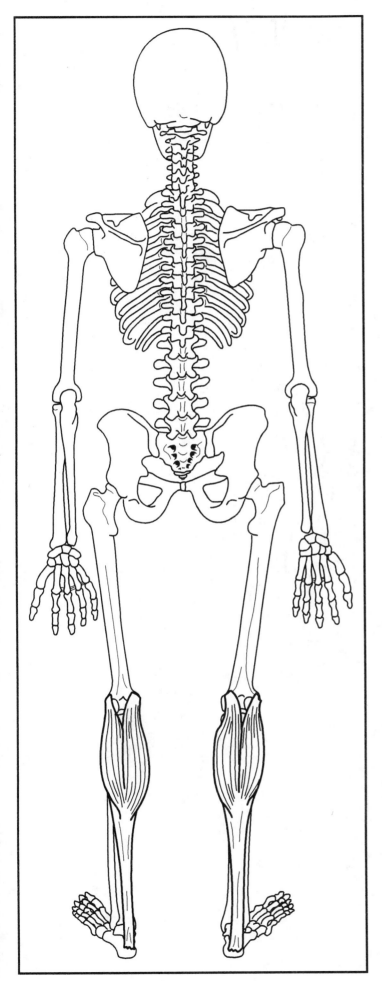

Gastrocnemius the Dinosaur has a favorite muscle, the gastrocnemius muscle.

It is called the gastrocnemius because the **"gastroc"** part of the name means **"belly"**, and the **"nemius"** part means **"leg"**. Therefore, gastrocnemius means **"the belly of the leg"**.

The gastrocnemius muscle is her favorite muscle because it helps her jump rope fast.

Find Your Gastrocnemius
Bend over and feel your calves (the back of your lower legs). Those are your gastrocnemius muscles. Now, stand on your toes. You can feel your gastrocnemius contract. When the gastrocnemius contracts, it flexes the foot at the ankle.

What activities does the gastrocnemius muscle help you do?
Jumping
Swimming
Running
Dancing

128

HAMSTRINGS

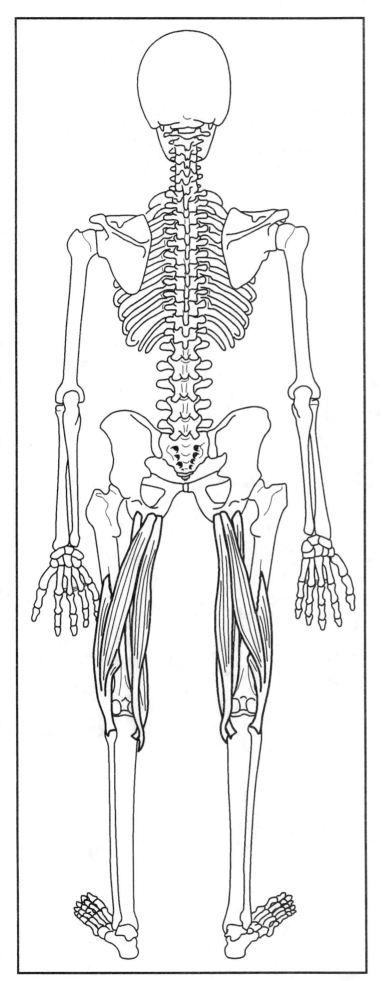

HAMSTRINGS
(the back of the thigh)
ham'strings

Hamstrings the Dinosaur has a favorite muscle group, the hamstrings.

"Hamstrings" is a nickname for the muscle group at the back of the thigh. They get their name because their tendons are long like strings.

The hamstrings are his favorite muscles because they help him run fast.

Find Your Hamstrings
Stand on one leg and lift the heel of the other leg. Feel behind your thigh, just above the back of your knee. You can feel the hamstring tendons. Now, lift your heel higher and you can feel the hamstring muscles work. The hamstrings flex the lower leg at the knee joint.

What activities do the hamstring muscles help you do?
Running
Swimming
Bicycling
Jumping
Skating

130

PECTORALIS MAJOR

131

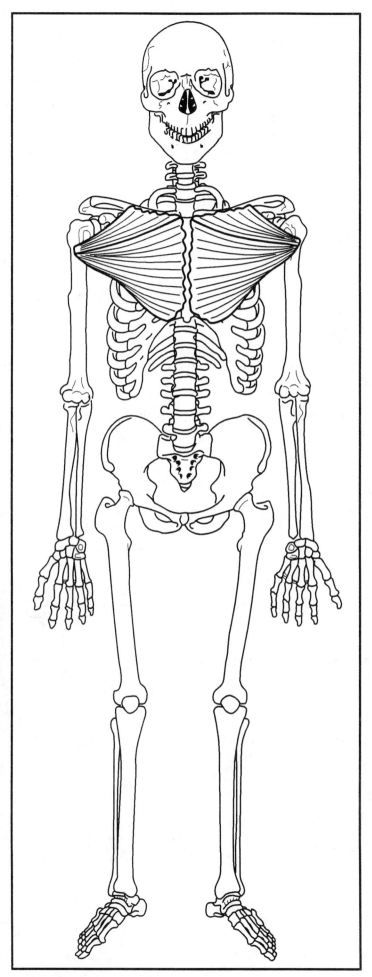

PECTORALIS MAJOR
(the chest)
pek"to-ra'lis ma'jer

Pectoralis Major the Dinosaur has a favorite muscle, the pectoralis major.

It is called the pectoralis major muscle because **"pectoralis"** means **"chest bone"**, which is where the muscle is attached. **"Major"** means **"larger"**. Therefore, pectoralis major means the **"larger muscle on the chest"**.

The pectoralis major is his favorite muscle because he loves to do a lot of push-ups.

Find Your Pectoralis Major
Put your arm straight out in front of you. Pinch the front of your armpit with your other hand. That is your pectoralis major muscle. Now, move your arm from side to side and you can feel your pectoralis major work. The pectoralis major muscle draws the arm forward at the shoulder joint.

What activities does the pectoralis major muscle help you do?
      Push-ups
      Swinging a bat
      Throwing
      Swinging a tennis racket

Getting Started

DAY 1

In order to have a successful experience, day 1 sets the tone for the entire program. Here's a few helpful pointers on how to spend day 1:

1 - SAFETY - It is imperative that you discuss, demonstrate, and engage the children in safe stepping techniques from the beginning.

> * Feet always atop the step. No heels hanging off the end of the steps. At times you'll want to call "FOOT CHECK" and have all children glance at their feet to check their placement.
>
> * Step quietly. No pounding feet or stomping.
>
> * Step down close to your step. Stepping far away places unnecessary stress on the children's backs.
>
> * Come to a full upright position when stepping atop the step. Avoid keeping the knees bent.
>
> * Don't jump down from the step. This high risk move jars the body and is unnecessary in this program.
>
> * Don't repeatedly step FORWARD off the step. This places a significant amount of stress on the front of the knee.

TRY IT OUT . . . Put on some music (118-122 beats per minute) and let the children explore their own movements on the step. Circulate the room and pay careful attention to their execution.

2 - RULES - Although our goal is to empower the children, they are still young children and need guidance and at times, discipline. Therefore, the ground rules and consequences for breaking the rules must be fully understood by all participants. You should get a large posterboard and print the rules and consequences on it. This posterboard should be exhibited and visible to all during EVERY class. It serves as a constant reminder to the children that only acceptable behavior is allowed and provides the EXACT consequence if unacceptable behavior arises. You can make up your own KidZ Step rules and consequences. Keep the list short and make sure all the rules are OBSERVABLE and SPECIFICALLY stated clearly. "Be nice" is vague and general. It means different things to different children. Here are some specific examples I've used in the past.

RULES

1. No "PUT DOWNS". You may not put anyone down by saying something that "hurts" another's feelings.

2. STOP, LOOK, LISTEN when one Whistle sound is heard.

3. SIT, HOLD, FOLD (sit down, hold all equipment in your hand, fold your hands/legs) when two Whistle sounds are heard.

4. No "Fighting"!

CONSEQUENCES

1. First Offense - 5 minutes in time out corner (Place a chair in a quiet corner area in the room "TIME OUT")

2. Second Offense - 15 minutes TIME OUT AND LOSS of one Incentive Sticker (You'll read how to use incentive stickers to motivate the children)

3. Third Offense - Parent Phone Conference

4. Fourth Offense - Temporary Suspension From Class

3 - INCENTIVE CHARTS/STICKERS - I use incentive charts and stickers

as motivators as well as a method for children to become responsible for their own progresses. Children enjoy the constant visual reinforcement of these charts. ALWAYS let the children affix their own stickers to their own charts. If you do it for them, it's not theirs, it's YOURS. One way to use the charts is:

Purchase individual charts for each child in the class. (The charts can be bought from any school supply store or from Creative Educational Materials, Telephone No. 1-612-455-7511). DO NOT ever use a class "roster" chart. A roster chart lists all the children on one chart and encourages "competition". (The child with the MOST stickers must be the BEST and the one with the LEAST, the WORST). For approximately $6 you can purchase individual charts and stickers for 30 children.

At the conclusion of each class, the children obtain a sticker for successfully participating in the class. At the end of the 12 week program, they can "cash-in" their stickers for a reward. You can decide what type of reward you'll give. Maybe it's "FREE PLAY" or a "TRINKET" from your magic bag. Keep a REWARDS sign posted as a constant reminder of the goals they're trying to attain. A sample reward chart might be:

REWARDS:

24 stickers = McDonald's gift certificate
20-30 stickers = "Trinket" from the Magic Box
12-19 stickers = FitKid Badge Button
10-11 stickers = FitKid Certificate and Smelly Sticker

My rewards change every 12 weeks so a new incentive motivator will keep their energies high

Where to Get Rewards Without Going Broke??

• Flea markets   • Garage sales   • Clearance sales   • Dollar stores

Use cookie sales, fun fairs, health fairs, walk-a-thons, etc. to raise money for a "Rewards" fund, rather than your personal funds.

Other Ideas . . .

Ask your local video store to donate a free video rental for all kids meeting their goals. The video store will LOVE the free advertising, the children LOVE videos.

Local merchants may be willing to donate products, money, etc. to your youth programs. Just ask!

Local ice cream stores may give FREE coupons. Check it out!

Area Karate expert may come in and give a FREE demonstration/activity session.

Offer trading cards (baseball, basketball, Barbie, etc.) as incentives.

For the older children, how about a "hair-do" class with a local beautician for the girls and a "skills n' drills tips" class with a local sports celebrity/athlete for the boys.

4 - FAMILY QUESTIONNAIRE/EMERGENCY FORM/ PERMISSION WAIVER/KIDZ SURVEY
(See following pages)

A Family Questionnaire gives you insight into the child's home life regarding their activity, their family's activities, as well as general health habits. This insight provides valuable information, and should be kept for future reference.

An Emergency Form and Permission Waiver furnishes you with a liability release for the child to participate in the program as well as a screening mechanism regarding the childs overall health and history of disease.

The Music and Moves Survey is used with the Level 2 KidZ Step to provide information on the child's music preferences and repertoire of movements.

5 - THE HOME LINK - FAMILY CALENDARS/CONTRACTS

The family calendar and signed contracts are just one way to involve the child's family in this exciting program. Feel free to use the enclosed materials to link your families to your program, which will help reinforce and support your efforts. This information should be explained on the first day.

FAMILY QUESTIONNAIRE

Please answer the following questions honestly, as they will help me understand your child's health and physical fitness needs.

Sincerely,

Youth Fitness Specialist

1. What physical activities does your child engage in on a regular basis?

_____ running   _____ active playing   _____ dance

_____ sports (list them _____)   _____ karate

_____ others _____

2. How many hours of physical activity does your child participate in daily?

_____ less than 1 hour/day   _____ from 1-3 hours/day

_____ from 3-5 hours/day   _____ more than 5 hours/day

3. Does your child like to move? _____

4. What sedentary activities does your child engage in?

_____ reading   _____ TV   _____ Nintendo

_____ board games   _____ others _____

5. How many hours of TV/Nintendo/board games/reading does your child engage in daily?

_____ less than 1 hour/day   _____ from 1-3 hours/day

_____ from 3-5 hours/day   _____ more than 5 hours/day

6. List all physical activities parents engage in.

_____
_____
_____

7. List the physical activities parents engage in with your child.

_____
_____
_____

FAMILY QUESTIONNAIRE

8. Does your child eat breakfast? _____

    If yes, what does he/she normally eat? _____
    _____

9. What does your child eat? (Check all that apply) _____

    _____ fried foods   _____ fresh fish   _____ boiled or baked foods

    _____ cheeses   _____ chips   _____ cookies/cakes

    _____ vegetables   _____ fruits   _____ pasta/rice

    _____ salads   _____ butter/oils/dressings

    _____ other _____

Your Name _____

Your Child's Name _____

EMERGENCY FORM/WAIVER

Your Name _____

Your Child's Name _____

Address _____

City/State/Zip _____

Home Phone _____

Work Phone _____

In case of an emergency, please contact:

Name _____
Relation to Child _____
Phone Number _____

OR

Name _____
Relation to Child _____
Phone Number _____

My child's physician is:
Name _____
Phone Number _____

I, _____, hereby grant permission to my child, _____, to participate in the KidZ Step program. I understand and agree to hold harmless, all instructors, assistants, aides, managers, and all affiliates to the KidZ Step program for any and all injuries that may result from this program.

_____   _____
Date   Signature

HEALTH HISTORY SURVEY

Child's Name _____

Please check off any and all health concerns that may affect his/her participation in the KidZ Step program.

_____ Severe Allergies (list them _____)

_____ Asthma (any medications? _____)

_____ Congenital Heart Problems

_____ High Blood Pressure

_____ Orthopedic Concerns (list them _____)

_____ Seizures (such as _____)

_____ Other _____

My child takes the following medications regularly:

_____

My child is allergic to:

_____

KIDZ SURVEY
Music and Moves

List your top ten favorite songs and their artists.

1.

2.

3.

4.

5.

6.

7.

8.

9.

10.

List your 5 favorite physical activities. (For example, football, dancing, rollerskating, etc.)

1.

2.

3.

4.

5.

The Home Link

Connecting KidZ Step to the home is a unique and vital component of this program. The following handouts are samples of ways to involve the entire family in this exciting program. Feel free to reproduce them.

Dear Mom and/or Dad:

I am beginning a new physical fitness program called KidZ Step. It is a fun and exciting exercise program for children. I want to participate in the KidZ Step program because it will teach me good healthy lifelong habits, strengthen all my muscles, make my heart stronger, and let me have FUN! I also want you to be physically fit. I love you very much and want you to live a long healthy life with me. Therefore, together we will complete the daily family fitness activity that will be found on my monthly calendar. At the end of the month, I can turn in the completed calendar and receive a certificate award for our family as well as get a special award for myself. Our family will feel better, have more energy, and become closer if we work and play together the KidZ Step way. By signing this official contract, we all agree to be a healthier, fitter family. We will all work together, support and encourage each other, and reap the many rewards of family fitness. YEAH!!!!

Love,

_____

All family members sign below. Thanks!

_____
Sign Here   Date

_____
Sign Here   Date

_____
Sign Here   Date

_____
Sign Here   Date

Family Fitness Calendar

This Family Fitness Calendar is to be sent home on the first day of the week, so the family can begin immediately. The family is to post the calendar on the refrigerator. The children place a "smiley face" on the dates that the activities have been honestly completed. Let them know that "cheating" will only "ROB" their family of valuable benefits. At the end of the month, the children turn in their calendars. The 100% completed calendars get "Family Fitness Certificates". The others can get "Honorable Mentions" or "Family Participant Certificates" if they made an attempt. Additionally, an individual child certificate can be provided. You can decide what the "criteria" will be for individual child certificates. Here's an example of my Individual Incentive Awards.

Incentive Awards

100% - Family GOLD Certificate. Individual 15 minutes of FREE PLAY plus 1 DIG for treasures. (I have a treasure chest full of trinkets)

80% - Family Participate Certificate. Individual receives "Scratch n Sniff" Super Kid sticker badge.

Family Fitness Calendar
Week 1

MONDAY	Give 3 x 2 hugs to a family member. How many hugs did you give? _____
TUESDAY	Everyone does 40 curl ups today counting by 2's. How many curl ups did you do? _____
WEDNESDAY	Walk around the block TWICE with your mom/or dad. Count the number of red cars you see. How many were there? _____
THURSDAY	Everyone does 20 - 8 pushups. How many did your whole family do? _____
FRIDAY	Walk around the block TWICE today and read every sign you see.
SATURDAY	Go for a 15 minute walk with a family member. What animals did you see? _____
SUNDAY	Everyone eats a piece of FRUIT after dinner. How many pieces of fruit did your whole family eat? _____

Family Fitness Calendar
Week 2

MONDAY	No CHIPS Day!!! Only eat pretzels, popcorn, fruit, or yogurt for snacks today. What snacks did you eat today? _____
TUESDAY	Do 2 MOVING Activities with your mom and/or dad for 15 minutes. (Ex. walking, dancing, biking, running, etc.) What 2 activities did you do? _____
WEDNESDAY	Give 5-1 hugs to a family member and say I Love You. How many hugs did you give? _____
THURSDAY	It's SPINACH Day!!! Yeah! Everyone eats spinach today. What vitamins are in spinach? _____
FRIDAY	EVERYBODY DANCE! 15 minutes of dancing with mom and/or dad today. What songs did you dance to? _____
SATURDAY	Play catch or IT with your mom/dad for 15 minutes today. Who did you play with? _____ What did you play? _____
SUNDAY	Walk around the block THREE times today with your mom/dad. How long did it take you? _____

Family Fitness Calendar
Week 3

MONDAY	Walk for 15 minutes outside with our mom/dad. What living things did you see? _____
TUESDAY	It's FRUIT DAY!!! Everyone eats TWO pieces of fruit today. How many family members are in your family? _____ Write the mathematical equation that represents how many pieces of fruit your family will eat today. _____
WEDNESDAY	FOLLOW ME DAY!! Your mom/dad must follow your "Moving" activities outside in your yard for 15 minutes. (Ex. running, hopping, jumping, etc.)
THURSDAY	CURL UP DAY!! Everyone does 10 x 2 curl ups to your favorite song. How many curl ups did you do? _____
FRIDAY	Give 10 - 3 - 4 hugs to a family member. How many hugs did you give? _____
SATURDAY	WATER DAY!!! Fill a LARGE jug with water and put it in the refridgerator this morning. Make sure everyone pitches in to drink it by evening. What time did you finally empty the jug? _____
SUNDAY	Walk around the block THREE times today and give a hug to those family members who walked with you. How many hugs did you give? _____

Family Fitness Calendar
Week 4

MONDAY	CURL UP DAY!! Everyone does curl ups for 1 minute. Total how many each family member did. What is your family total? _____ How many people are in your family? _____
TUESDAY	Give 4 + 3 - 2 hugs to a family member. How many hugs did you give? _____
WEDNESDAY	Give 5-1 hugs to a family member and say I Love You. How many hugs did you give? _____
THURSDAY	FOLLOW THE LEADER DAY!!! You must follow your mom/dad's moving activities for 15 minutes. (Ex. running, jogging, walking, etc.) What was your favorite activity that you did? _____
FRIDAY	VEGGIE DAY!!! Eat vegetables with lunch and dinner. What color vegetables did you eat today? _____
SATURDAY	PUSHUP DAY!!! Everyone does 16 pushups today. Ready set GO!!!!
SUNDAY	Walk for 15 minutes with a family member. How many blocks did you walk? _____ How many people with brown hair did you see? _____

Family Fitness Certificate

Congratulations to the _____ Family

for successfully completing four weeks

of fun, family, fitness activities.

Place Gold Seal Here

_____
Authorized Signature

_____
Date

Family Participant Certificate

This certificate acknowledges that the

_____ Family has

participated in four weeks of

fun, family, fitness activities.

Authorized Signature

Date

HURRAY

Congratulations to _____

for being a Great KidZ Stepper.

Welcome to the KidZ Step Alumni Club.

_____
Authorized Signature

_____
Date

Research

Numerous fitness tests performed over the past twenty years have generated concerns about the fitness levels of American children, (Safrit, 1986). Present information suggests an important role for exercise in children's health, but effectively guiding today's youth into active lifestyles will require a much greater scientific foundation than is currently available, (Rowland, 1990).

Many research studies on children's health and fitness are still controversial, (Rowland, 1990). Despite these shortcomings, this chapter will present an overview of the current research available and its implication for us, the youth fitness specialists, in planning safe and effective children's programs. We must be aware that some of the current information available on children and exercise will be reassessed in the near future as more studies are being undertaken to fully understand children's health and fitness as preventative measures for adult diseases.

Field Study Overview

A ten week study was undertaken with sixty four 6th graders (ages 10-11) at Taylor School, a Chicago Public School located in the heart of a lower/middle class neighborhood on the south side of Chicago. The control group (31 children) engaged in normal gym activities for the entire length of the study. The normal gym activity was "Pillow Polo", a take off on floor hockey. The control group played Pillow Polo twice a week for 45 minutes per session. The experimental group (33 children) engaged in the KIDZ Step Level 2 Group Step Program twice weekly for 45 minutes per session.

Pre/Post Test

Both groups were tested for height, weight, pre exercise pulse, pre exercise blood pressure, aerobic endurance (1 mile walk/run), muscular strength (modified pullups), and body composition (skinfold calipers). The methods of assessment, equipment, and testers, were identical both pre and post test. The only variable that was difficult to control was the heat/humidity outdoors for the 1 mile walk/run. The pretest outdoor environment was 70 degrees with 80% humidity with overcast cloud coverings. The posttest outdoor environment was 82 degrees with 85% humidity with overcast cloud coverings.

Results

The data was interpreted by Scott Roberts M.S., pediatric exercise physiologist. The preliminary results showed significant differences in weight, pullups, mile run/walk, body composition and pulse rates between the control and experimental groups. Height increased in both groups, due to normal growth and development of prepubescent youth. Blood pressure showed no significant difference between the groups.

For a detailed study and abstract, please write:

> **BodyWorks KIDZ Step**
> **12916 Commercial**
> **Chicago, Illinois 60633**

Not only does obesity affect the physical being of children, it also has psychosocial consequences as well, (Rowland, 1990). In 1980, Allon reported that obesity influenced mental health. Both Allon (1980) and Williams (1986) agree that childhood obesity may increase depression, cause low self esteem, poor body image, and social isolation. Just think back to your own childhood memories. Was the "fattest" child the most popular and most outgoing in your class? Not in mine.

Extensive experience has demonstrated that exercise can be an effective means of reducing fat in obese children with or without specific dietary restriction, (Rowland, 1990).

Some obesity theorists argue that the difficulty in achieving weight loss in obese individuals is determined by the number of fat cells rather than their size, (Rowland, 1990). Knittle and Ginsberg-Freeman (1980) demonstrated that a combination of exercise and diet with young obese children can stabilize fat cell numbers as well as long term weight gain. Oscai et.al. (1974) studied animals and have found that young rats in regular swimming programs during the first month of life demonstrated lower fat cell counts than either dieting or control group animals.

Overall Precautions

HEAT
Children do not respond well physiologically to heat stress, compared to adults (Bar-Or 1980, 1984). Therefore, particular attention needs to be placed to fluid replacement (water) before, during, and after exercise as well as environmental conditions while exercising (i.e. heat, humidity).

GROWING
Growth of the long bones occurs primarily in the cartilage of the epiphyseal plate. These growth centers are vulnerable to traumatic injury because their strength is estimated to be 2-5 times less than that of the surrounding fibrous joint capsule and ligament (Caine & Lindner, 1984). Amidst a significant body of research, the verdict is still out regarding growth plate injury risk and physical activity and training. Currently, there is no direct evidence that even intense exercise regimens can be expected to produce microtraumatic injury (Rowland 1990). At this point, it is recommended to heed "caution" regarding intense repetitive stressful training until further research proves differently.

For Your Information . . .

This section will provide you with valuable resources as well as an extensive bibliography. It concludes with some information about the program developer, Debbie Ban-Pillarella and a list of acknowledgments.

RESOURCES

The following resources can supply you with the equipment, props, and incentives for your program.

Creative Educational Materials (Stickers, Certificates, Incentives)
612-455-7511
PO Box 18127
West St. Paul, MN 55118

Dino-Muscles (Youth Anatomy and Kinesiology Lessons)
PO Box 4019
Laguna Beach, CA 92652
1-800-947-KNOW

Dyna Mixx Music Service (Youth Fitness Music)
1-800-THE-MIXX

International Kids Fitness Association
27 West 20th Street
Suite 1207
New York, NY 10011
1-800-926-8878

Today's Fitness Step (Childrens' Steps)
1-800-851-6373
1500 W. Hampden 5C
Englewood, CO 80110

SPRI Products
(Portable, Resistive Products - QuikFits)
708-537-7876
1554 Barclay Boulevard
Buffalo Grove, IL 60089

BIBLIOGRAPHY

Abraham, S., & Nordsieck, M., (1960) Relationship of excess weight in children and adults. Public Health Reports, 75: 263-273.

Allon, N. (1980) Sociological aspects of overweight youth. In PJ Collipp (ed.) Childhood Obesity (3rd ed. pg 139-156), PSG Publishing, Littleton, MA

American Alliance for Health, Physical Education, Recreation, and Dance (1980). Health related physical fitness test manual. Reston, VA.

American Alliance for Health, Physical Education, Recreation, and Dance (1988). Physical Best. Reston, VA.

Astrand, P., (1952) Experimental studies of physical work capacity in relationship to sex and age. Copenhagen: Munksgaard.

Carey, J., Hager, M., Harrison, J. Failing In Fitness, Newsweek, April 1985, 84-87.

Clippenger-Robertson, K., Durrett, A., Staver, P. (1992) Captivate Kids With Exercise, IDEA Today, September 1992.

Corbin, C.B. (1987) Physical Fitness in K-12 curriculum: Some defensible solutions to perennial problems. Journal of Physical Education, Recreation, and Dance, 58 (7), 49-54.

Cumming, G.R., Everatt, D., Hastman, L., (1978) Bruce treadmill test in children: Normal values in a clinic population. Journal of Cardiology 41: 69-75.

Davies, C. (1980) Metabolic cost of exercise and physical performance in children with some observations on external loading. European Journal of Applied Physiology, 45: 95-102.

Day, L. (1981) The testing, prediction, and significance of maximum aerobic power in children. Australia Journal of Sport Sciences, 1: 18-22.

Dietz, W. (1983) Childhood Obesity: Susceptibility, cause, and management. Journal of Pediatrics, 103: 676-686.

Dietz W., Gortmaker, S., (1985) Do we fatten our children at the television set? Obesity and television viewing in children and adolescents, Pediatrics, 75: 807-811.

Dietz W., Gortmaker, S., (1984) Factors within the physical environment associated with childhood obesity. American Journal of Clinical Nutrition, 39: 619-624.

Drabman, R., Hammer, D., Jarvie, G., (1977) Eating rates of elementary school children. Journal of Nutrition Education, 9:80-82.

Fit Youth Today (1986), Fit Youth Today Program Manual, Austin, TX, American Health and Fitness Foundation.

Franks, Don. YMCA Youth Fitness Test Manual (1989). Human Kinetics Publisher, Inc.

Franks, B.D., Morrow J.R., Plowman, S.A., (1989), Youth Fitness Testing: Politics Validation and Planning, QUEST 40 (2) 187-199.

BIBLIOGRAPHY
(Continued)

Gillman, T.B., Freedson, P.S., Geenan, D.L., Shahraray, B., (1981) Physical activity patterns determined by heart rate monitoring in 6-7 year old children. Medicine and Science in Sports and Exercise, 13: 65-67.

Gober, B.E., & Franks, B.D., (1988) The physical and fitness education of young children. Journal of Physical Education, Recreation, and Dance, 59 (7) 57-61.

Going, S. (1988) Physical Best: Body composition in assessment of youth fitness. Journal of Physical Education, Recreation, and Dance 59 (7) 32-36.

Holman, R., McGill, H., Geer, G.C., (1958) The natural history of atherosclerosis: The early aortic lesions as seen in New Orleans in the middle of the 20th Century. American Journal of Pathology, 34: 209-235.

Institute For Aerobic Research (1988), Fitnessgram. Dallas, TX.

Klesges, R., Shelton, M., Klesges, M., (1993) Effects of television on metabolic rates: potential implications for childhood obesity. Pediatrics, 2: 281-286.

Knittle, J., (1972) Obesity in childhood: a problem in adipose tissue cellular development. Journal of Pediatrics, 6: 1048-1059.

Knittle, J.L., Ginsberg-Fellner, F., (1980) Can obesity be prevented? In PJ Collipp (Ed) Childhood Obesity (2nd ed. pg 63-78), PSG Publishing, LIttleton, MA.

Larson-Gustafson, A., Terry, R., (1992) Weight related behaviors and concerns of 4th grade children. Journal of American Dietetic Association, 92: 818-822.

Lloyd, JK., Wolff, O., Whelen, W., (1961) Childhood Obesity: A long term study of height and weight. British Medical Journal, 7: 142-148.

Lohman, T.G. (1987) Use of skinfolds to estimate body fatness in children and youth. Journal of Physical Education, Recreation, and Dance, 58 (9) 98-102.

Lowenstein, M., (1987) Weight reduction techniques in the pediatric patient. Topics in Clinical Nutrition, 2: 49-54.

Mullins, A., (1958) The prognosis in juvenile obesity. Archives of Disease of Childhood, 33: 307-314.

Newman, W.P., Strong J.P., (1978) Natural history, geographic pathology, and pediatric aspects of atherosclerosis. In W.B. Strong (ed.) Atherosclerosis: Its Pediatric Aspects (pg 15-40), New York: Grunne and Stratton.

Oscai, L., Babirak S.P., Dubach, F.B., (1974) Exercise or food restriction: Effect on adipose tissue cellularity. American Journal of Physiology, 277: 901-904.

Paffenbarger, R.S., Hyde, R.T. (1984) Exercise in the prevention of coronary heart disease. Preventative Medicine, 13: 3-22.

Patterson, R., Typpo, J., Krause, G., (1986), Factors related to obesity in preschool children. Journal of American Dietetic Association, 86: 1376-1381.

Rians, C., Weltman, A., Cahill, B., Janney, C., Tippett, S., Katch, F., (1987) Strength training for prepubescent males. Is it safe? American Journal of Sports Medicine, 15: 483-489.

Riopel, D., Tayler, A., Hohn, A., (1979) Blood pressure, heart rate, pressure-rate product and electrocardiographic changes in healthy children during treadmill exercise. American Journal of Cardiology, 44: 697-703.

Rowland, T., (1990) Exercise and Children's Health. Human Kinetics, Champaign, IL. Sharkey, Kinetics, Champaign, IL.

Sewall L., Micheli, L., (1986) Strength training for children. Journal of Pediatric Orthopedics, 6: 143-146.

Shepard, R.J., et.al. (1969) The working capacity of Toronto school children. Canadian Medical Association Journal, 100: 560-566.

Simonson, F., (1982) Advances in research and treatment of obesity. Food and Nutrition News, 53: 1-4.

Sintek, S., Bishop, P., (1985) Physicians perceptions of using physical education for managing childhood obesity. Physician and Sports Medicine, 5: 119-124.

Snell, P.G., Mitchell, J.H., (1984) The role of maximum oxygen uptake in exercise performance. Clinics in Chest Medicine, 5: 51-62.

Stark, O., Atkins, E., Wolff, O., Douglas, J., (1981) Longitudinal study of obesity in National Survey of Health and Development. British Medical Journal, 283: 13-17.

Walburg, J., Ward, D., (1985) Role of physical activity in the etiology and treatment of childhood obesity. Pediatrician, 12: 82-88.

Ward, D., Bar-Or O., (1986) Role of physician and physical education teacher in treatment of obesity at school. Pediatrician, 13: 44-51.

Washington, R., VanGundy J., Cohen, C., Sondheimer, H., Wolfe, R., (1988) Normal aerobic and anaerobic exercise data for North American school-age children. Journal of Pediatrics, 112: 223-233.

Weinhaus, R., (1969) The management of obesity: Some recent concepts. Missouri Medicine 66: 719-730.

Weltman, A., Janny, C., Rians, C., Strand, K., Berg, B., Tippitts, S., Wise, J., Cahill, B., Katch, F., (1986) The effects of hydraulic resistance strength training in prepubertal males.

Wilmore, J.H. (1986), Sensible Fitness, Human Kinetics, Champaign, IL.

Williams, M.H., (1986) Weight control through exercise and diet for children and young athletes. In G.A. Stull & H.M. Eckert (Eds) Effects of Physical Activity on Children (pg 88-133) Human Kinetics, Champaign, IL

Winich, M., (1974) Childhood Obesity. Nutrition Today, May/June: 6-12.

161